Princess of Orange

Books for Young Readers
by Elisabeth Kyle

PRINCESS OF ORANGE
THE SWEDISH NIGHTINGALE: Jenny Lind
GIRL WITH A PEN: Charlotte Bronte

Princess of Orange
by Elisabeth Kyle

HOLT, RINEHART AND WINSTON

New York   Chicago   San Francisco

921
M

For my Friends at the Tucker House
Williamsburg

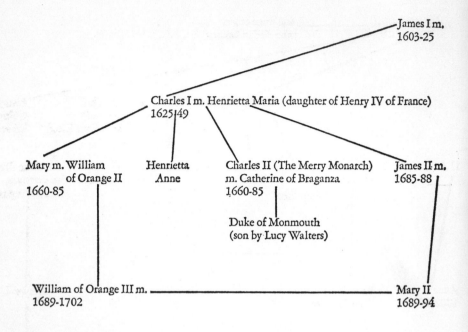

James I m.
1603-25

Charles I m. Henrietta Maria (daughter of Henry IV of France)
1625-49

Mary m. William
of Orange II
1660-85

Henrietta
Anne

Charles II (The Merry Monarch)
m. Catherine of Braganza
1660-85

James II m.
1685-88

Duke of Monmouth
(son by Lucy Walters)

William of Orange III m.
1689-1702

Mary II
1689-94

The dates are those
of lengths of reigns

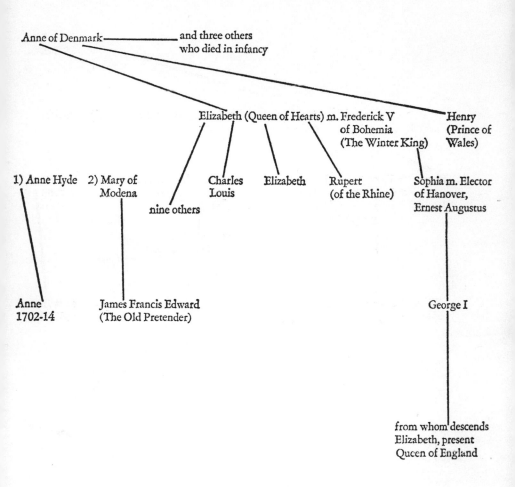

Anne of Denmark ————————— and three others
who died in infancy

Elizabeth (Queen of Hearts) m. Frederick V
of Bohemia
(The Winter King)

Henry
(Prince of
Wales)

1) Anne Hyde   2) Mary of
Modena

Charles
Louis

Elizabeth

Rupert
(of the Rhine)

Sophia m. Elector
of Hanover,
Ernest Augustus

nine others

Anne
1702-14

James Francis Edward
(The Old Pretender)

George I

from whom descends
Elizabeth, present
Queen of England

 Chapter
One

Richmond in the autumn of 1673.

The Forest was turning gold and losing its leaves. The three girls ran toward it, down the slope of the fields with the towers of Richmond Palace behind them. They ran in age order, but not on that account. Sarah Jennings led the way because she always did. Then came Mary, then Anne who, besides being the youngest, was also very round and fat.

They were running away. Two of them were princesses, and the third, Sarah Jennings, was nobody in particular, whom the King allowed to be educated along with his nieces. Their governess, Lady Frances Villiers, had one of her bad headaches, so they had escaped from her vigilance. The sooner they reached the shelter of the trees the better, in case Lady Frances looked out of her window and saw them. . . .

Anne stumbled and sat down suddenly. She began to bawl. Sarah turned back and jerked the little girl to her feet saying, "Hold your noise!"

Mary, Anne's sister turned back too. She was two years younger than Sarah, but tall for her age and very graceful. Usually she was gentle, too. But now she spoke sharply. "You must not speak like that to my sister. It would be best if you remembered, sometimes, who she is."

Sarah dropped a sudden, mocking curtsey. "I beg your Highness's pardon. And of course, the Princess Anne's."

Sarah was extraordinarily pretty already. She had a dazzling skin, greenish eyes and auburn hair. She had also a violent temper, and her own way to make in the world. While the other two were merely escaping for an hour or two's fun, Sarah knew exactly why she wanted to reach the Forest.

Her quick ears had caught the sound of the hunting horn. Somewhere, in the depth of the Forest, the King and his friends were riding. It was late afternoon now. Soon the hunting party would dismount to eat a lavish meal under the trees. The gentlemen of the court liked Sarah because of her ready tongue and her beauty. She knew on which side her bread was buttered, and besides, she wanted to join in the fun. . . .

Anne had picked herself up; was glaring, not at Sarah but at her sister.

"Sarah's my friend. I don't *want* her to remember who I am!"

Indeed, the little girl had been fascinated by Sarah as long as she had known her. She would trot all day humbly at her heels, receiving in return nothing but a half-playful contempt. Anne's sister Mary, having regained her usual sweet temper, merely picked up her long skirts again and began to walk across the stubble toward the fringe of giant oaks before them.

Anne was obsessed by Sarah. She would grow out of it.

Nearer this time came the sound of the horn. The three girls stopped for a moment, listening. Then Sarah began to hurry forward again. "His Majesty's coming this way!" She called over her shoulder.

The King. Mary felt a flat feeling of disappointment as she stepped at last into the cool shade of the trees. She had hoped it would be her father, the Duke of York. That stately melancholic gentleman had decided that his two motherless daughters would grow up stronger in the sweet air of Richmond, though he himself had to live in London. So Mary and Anne saw him seldom.

And Mary had, somehow, counted upon his hunting in this direction so as to sup with them afterward. So had Anne. For once she spoke indignantly to Sarah. "Why Uncle King? Why not Father?"

Of course Mary had known why not. But she had forgotten. Now she exchanged glances with Sarah over Anne's head. There was a pause, while the autumn sunshine slanted down at them through the trees and a leaf or two dropped at their feet.

At last Sarah muttered, "You had best tell her. She must know soon."

"Lady Frances said——"

"Are you not the Duke's daughter? Who else should tell her but her own sister!"

"Tell me what?" Anne tugged at Mary's hand. No use now, withholding what the whole court had known now for weeks.

"Anne sweetheart, you know our father has been very lonely since Mama died?"

"Has he?" Anne looked doubtful. "If he was lonely, he could have come oftener to see us."

"He's been too busy fighting against the Dutch. You wouldn't have liked the Dutch to sail their ships right up the river, the way they did before?"

Anne shook her head. The plump face hardened suddenly. "Fighting our bad cousin William. He's Dutch."

"But now things are a little better. So Papa is going to get married again."

Anne digested this in silence. Presently she asked, "Who is he going to marry? Somebody nice?"

"An Italian princess. Everyone says she's——"

"She's a Papist," Sarah, tired of being left out of the conversation, broke in suddenly. "Your new stepmother's a Catholic like your father. Lord! What fools some folk can be!"

Mary straightened up suddenly. Again a look of unaccustomed anger crossed her face. Seeing it, Sarah wished not for the first time, that Anne had been the elder of

the two sisters. Anne she could wind round her little fin-
ger. But it was Mary not Anne, who might be going to be
Queen someday. . . . And Mary had always seen through
Sarah. She was much more intelligent than Anne.

Mary was saying coldly, "Do you call my father a fool?"

Sarah had gone too far and she knew it. She said in
sulky tones, "Well, the country won't stand for a Catholic
sovereign. That's why King Charles ordered you and
Anne to be brought up Protestant——"

"Be quiet!" Mary interrupted her sharply. "My father
and no one else is heir to the throne!"

"If the country will have him," Sarah muttered under
her breath. She was sharp enough and old enough to pick
up the scraps of gossip brought down from the Court of St.
James's from time to time. She knew the country disliked
and feared the handsome Duke of York; feared his obstinacy and stupidity. Feared lest, when he came to the
throne, he would take away that very freedom of religion
which permitted him to cling to his own.

Why, even the King knew what the country thought!
Sarah's mouth twitched as she remembered Charles's remark to his brother who had been begging him not to
walk about unguarded for fear of assassination.

"Nobody's going to assassinate me in order to put you
on the throne, James!"

It was both witty and true. Sarah could appreciate the
King's wit just as the Duke's stupidity bored her, for all
that the Duke was so handsome, and the King so swarthy
and ugly. . . .

Anne was repeating in her dogged, monotonous little voice, "Why Uncle King? Why not Father?"

Mary said, "Because our new stepmother is in England and Father must pay her attention instead of us. They are getting acquainted with each other——"

"Besides," Sarah broke in maliciously, "they say she can't speak English yet. The London Court won't like that. She's down at Dover, learning her lessons and there she'll have to stay till she does speak English!"

Mary wished no more discussion on the subject. She was tired of the gossip that had flooded St. James's and trickled down the river toward Richmond. Lady Frances Villiers had forbidden the subject to be mentioned before Anne. The royal governess wanted her charges to meet their new stepmother quite unprejudiced. Mary, of course, had known, because she was more often with older people. And Sarah was adept at picking gossip out of the air.

The news seemed to make little impression upon Anne after all. She only asked indifferently, "Will our new stepmother give us nice things to eat?"

They had entered on a narrow path leading through the Forest and once more had to walk singly. In their long, sweeping skirts (even Anne had to hold hers up with both hands) and their fashionable attire they looked like young court ladies already. Yet Sarah, for all her grown-up boldness was only thirteen. Mary, who led the way this time, was two years younger, but no one would have guessed it, for she was extremely tall, like her famous and beautiful great-grandmother, Mary Queen of Scots. Where that first

Mary had been fair and red-haired, however, Mary's hair was blue-black, and her beautiful, shortsighted eyes were velvety black as well.

Anne was shortsighted too. She screwed up her eyes as she ran, for the trees cast confusing shadows like stripes over the path. She was only nine.

Presently the path opened onto a wider track or carriageway. They knew it well. It was the track used by the little carriages that sometimes followed the hunting parties, bearing the ladies of the court. The carriages would make for an agreed spot, and a picnic meal would be served there.

But today no fresh wheel ruts were to be seen. The girls noticed this at once. Besides, the carriages must set out from Richmond if the hunt was to take place on this side of the Forest. The King preferred to hunt on this side, so . . .

"Perhaps it's Father after all," said Anne hopefully.

Mary's large dark eyes were peering uncertainly down the track. Where it narrowed to disappear into the trees again, something seemed to stand looking back at them. "There's a man there!" she exclaimed.

Sarah had spotted some mushrooms and was bending down to pick them. She did not hear what was said. Anne screwed up her eyes, shading them with one pudgy hand.

"It isn't a man. It's a tree," she said.

At the end of the path the figure moved. Detaching itself from the trees, it walked swiftly towards them. But the green flickering shadows disguised its face so that the short-sighted girls could not see who it was, even yet. Mary at least, felt sudden apprehension. Bad men, thieves, even murderers, hid themselves in the Park. And here the three of them were, alone and unprotected, very far away from the safety of Richmond Palace.

To hide her trepidation even from herself, Mary spoke sharply to Anne for once.

"Don't be silly. It moves, so it is a man."

"A man? Where?" Sarah sprang up, the mushrooms held in a corner of her skirt. The man had nearly reached them now, growing taller and handsomer with every step. Indeed he bore a likeness to Mary herself, for he had the same Stuart features and the same elegant gait. Young, lithe and just twenty-three.

"It's your cousin, Monmouth!" Sarah said instantly.

In her relief, Mary almost scolded Anne again. "You see? You were wrong. Quite wrong."

Anne stared obstinately at the figure approaching. She said, "I still think it's a tree."

The King's son who could never be king, reached them at last. He bowed, then smiled enchantingly at all three. No wonder his father, King Charles II, adored and spoiled him! But the King had not married the mother of this handsome, proud young Stuart, who was therefore not in the legitimate succession, as Mary was, and after her, Anne. All Charles could do was to create this best-beloved son of his Duke of Monmouth and give him everything he asked for.

"Well, Cousins! And Mistress Jennings—James Monmouth flashed her a glance—"I was sent to the palace to fetch you, but seeing you've walked so far already, can you walk a little farther? The Duke of York and his party are behind me. He wants to see you."

Mary held out her hand to him. He took it and kissed it gently. Between those two, so alike in looks, so different in character, there was a strong bond. "Where have you left your horse?" she asked.

"With the remounts. I've been in the saddle too long, I wanted to walk."

He turned and led the way back through the trees until presently voices came toward them, and a glimpse of the royal liveries. Then the hunting party burst into full view. Most of them had dismounted and were sitting with their backs against the trees, finishing a meal. The Duke of York rose to his feet when he saw the girls coming. He held out his arms and Anne, running past Mary, threw herself into them at once.

The handsome man disengaged himself. "And daughter Mary? No kiss from her?"

Mary walked forward slowly. There had been a time when she loved her father as impulsively as did Anne. But the talk around her had done its work. Talk of her father having turned Papist; and how he might ruin the country with his tyranny once his brother was dead. . . .

She still loved her father, but she wasn't sure of him any more. She held up her face obediently to be kissed. Now he was drawing out something from his pocket which caught the sun, something sparkling in its gold and diamond frame. "Look at this face," he invited. "Would she not make you a pretty playmate?"

The face in the miniature was bewitchingly pretty.

Mary handed the miniature back to her father. "What is her name?"

"Mary Beatrice, your new stepmother. She is only fifteen and has never been out of Italy before. Will you befriend her, Mary?"

Mary looked solemnly back at her father. "I will," she said.

The cavalcade was reforming itself to ride out from the trees toward the palace. Sarah had been lifted on to a pony belonging to one of the grooms, while Mary rode pillion in front of her cousin Monmouth, and the Duke of York's strong arm held his little daughter Anne safe in the saddle before him.

So they rode out of the shadow of the trees, over the fields now pink with the sunset, toward Richmond Palace with its turrets and gilded weather vanes that shone in the evening light. The others disappeared through the archway into the palace courtyard. But Monmouth reined his horse, jumped down and lifted Mary down after him. Then, leading the horse by the bridle, he signed to her to follow him along the path, fringed with reeds, which bordered the River Thames.

She obeyed, wondering. He said abruptly, "Your father is about to make another of his foolish blunders."

"Wh-what do you mean?"

"This marriage. He should have consulted Parliament and the country first. The country may swallow *him* as its next ruler. But she is a Catholic too and if they have a son, he will certainly be brought up so. That means a Catholic dynasty established, which nobody wants."

She was stung into defense of her father. "Of course you say so, being a Protestant——"

"Like yourself." He said coolly, adding with self-satisfaction, "They call me the Protestant Duke. And I'm the King's eldest son after all."

A swan sailed majestically past on the river. James Monmouth picked up a stone and flung it after the bird. "Although William's a Protestant too." He added more soberly, "They may prefer him."

She looked startled. "William? Our cousin William?"

"Yes, the nasty little fellow. If his fleet had got up the Thames as far as this he might have been King of England now."

She was not sure if the chill from the water had made her shiver, or if it was the thought of her cousin William whom she had never seen, but feared like everyone else. England had been at war with his country, Holland, as long as she could remember. The cannon of the Dutch fleet had roared their message almost as far as this. Then, thank God! the British navy had managed to turn them back. But it had been a near thing. . . .

"You have fought against William," she said. "What is he really like?"

"A good soldier first." Monmouth conceded the point. "After all, he's bound to have some qualities or the Dutch wouldn't have made him their Captain General at only twenty-two years of age."

"Is he—good-looking?"

Monmouth considered. "He has the Stuart face, but hardened and cold. He's fought too much in his life to have any agreeable qualities left. Except honesty of course, but that's so excessively dull!"

Mary drew her cloak closer about her. Surely it *was* cold down here by the river! She turned and began to make her way back to the palace. Mischievously, he called after her, "If it hadn't been for this war, you would have known very well what he was like!"

"Why?" she called back over her shoulder.

"Eleven years old is not too young to be affianced. Though it is perhaps a trifle young to become Princess of Orange."

She stopped, and turned an amazed face toward him. "What nonsense are you talking now? Princess of Orange!"

He was charmed to see the velvet-dark eyes brighten with anger for once. He noted the tautness of the hand clutching her cloak; a plump, childish hand still, yet with the elegance of a woman's. He caught hold of the other hand, pretending to read its palm.

"Your fate, my dear cousin! If ever we make peace with Holland, you will be William's bride. Mark my words."

She wrenched her hand away and began to run toward the palace. He sauntered after her, smiling to himself. Just for the moment she looked more like her obstinate little sister Anne, or even the spitfire Sarah Jennings, than one could have believed possible. . . .

 Chapter
Two

Her story really begins here.

Richmond Forest merely cast its shadow over the early pages. The girls are all more than a year older by the end of this winter of 1674. They are in London now. Old Richmond Palace stands empty, the wind whirling its gilded weather vanes about and rustling the reeds down by the river.

Sarah at least, is considered a grown-up young lady and even Mary, at nearly thirteen, is treated as practically so. Girls grew up quickly in the reign of Charles the Second, and his Majesty wanted their help in performing a masque or court play in honor of their new stepmother. It would serve to lighten the dull days after Christmas.

So they had been brought up to London, though Lady
Frances did not really approve. The Palace of St. James's
hummed with rehearsals, with snatched bits of music, with
voices declaiming speeches and breaking down, to be
prompted again. And with the bustle of sewing the elaborate costumes which Mr. Gibson designed on his drawing
board.

He sat now as near to the window and the pale winter
light as he could get, drawing one of them. Hunched up,
half in the shadow of the curtains, one would not guess
what was the matter with him, unless one caught sight of
the little, misshapen legs tucked under his chair. He
looked burly, broad-shouldered, with a fine head, the hair
only faintly grizzled with gray.

Then he sprang up to retrieve a chalk that had slipped
through his fingers; and one saw that he was a dwarf, not
four feet high.

"Let me see the sketch! Please, dear Mr. Gibson, let
me see what I'm to wear!"

Mary tried to peep over his shoulder. They had all had
their drawing lessons from him and she, because she always protected him from mockery and treated him with
politeness, was his special favorite. Sarah Jennings he detested because she mocked him more than anyone else.

Had it been Sarah who asked him, he would have refused. Because it was Mary, he held the drawing board out
for her to see.

"That's the dress for your Highness." He pointed a
stubby finger at the nymphlike creature he had drawn. Its

floating draperies were colored in chalk. The dress was to be soft greenish-blue with shell-pink silk draperies forming a classical robe right down to her feet.

"There. That will set off your Highness' coloring and eyes."

"How grown-up and grand I shall look!" She clapped her hands.

The dwarf looked pleased. The other costume designs lay on the window sill beside him. There were to be five other girls taking part, besides Mary and Anne. A few professional actors and actresses had been engaged to give extra polish to some of the scenes. But the star of the cast would certainly be James Monmouth. He was the only person at court whose acting was of professional standard. And he was easily the finest dancer in London.

"Show me my dress! And Sarah's." Anne wriggled past her sister, trying to reach the finished drawings on the sill. Richard Gibson selected two and handed them over to her. She held them up, one after the other, to her near-sighted eyes. She was to be a goddess, rather a plump one, but the idea pleased her. All the same, Mr. Gibson had not spent so much pains on their costumes. He much preferred Mary to Anne.

Still, Anne was satisfied enough at being given floating draperies too, and a dress down to her toes. It was when she looked at the second sketch that she grew angry.

"You've dressed Sarah in such a hideous color, considering her hair is red! You must change it. I won't have Sarah looking a fright."

"She'll look well enough," the dwarf muttered. "Well enough for a jumped-up nobody!"

Mary watched her small sister with alarm. Anne, usually so phlegmatic and slow to react, had pursed up her mouth with rage. "She's my best friend! You will not dress my best friend like that!" She snatched a crayon from the box beside Mr. Gibson and before anyone could stop her, had scribbled wildly over the offending sketch.

"*Anne!*"

The door burst open, interrupting them. Sarah marched in, whistling like a boy. She whistled beautifully. Anne burst into tears as she ran toward her friend, exclaiming, "Look what he's done! He wanted to make a merry-andrew of you, but I stopped it!"

Sarah looked at the sketch on the drawing board and burst out laughing. At fourteen she was already very beautiful in a fair, dashing manner which contrasted with Mary's dark, gentle grace. Sarah still had a violent temper which, however, did not show itself often. In fact, one never knew if she would be angry, or laugh.

Mary, who hated rows, drew a deep breath of relief. Sarah lifted the costume sketch from the drawing board, smiled again at Anne's chalky scribbles, then deliberately tore up the sketch and dropped the pieces on the floor.

"A wasted effort," she remarked, "seeing no matter what Gibson draws, I shall wear what I like for the Masque. Come Anne, let us go somewhere else more amusing."

The dwarf and the princess looked at each other as

Sarah's whistling died down the passage. Then Richard Gibson shrugged his shoulders, began pinning a fresh paper onto the drawing board. "It will be a bold man who will tame *her*," he muttered.

Mary left the room with the sketch of her own costume, which she must take to one of the sewing women to make up. There was far too little time before the performance. The King had given them only a month, and half the month was gone already. Anne had one or two quite long speeches to make, and Mary must coach her. Anne was dumpy and would always be ungraceful compared with her sister. But one gift she had; the gift of a beautiful voice. So they had given her speeches to say, while Mary would sing and dance.

She went through the corridors, looking for Anne. St. James's Palace was darker and smokier, and smelt more than at Richmond, where the pure air blew in from the Park. Mary wrinkled up her nose. Others might not notice smells as she did, they were so well accustomed to them, even in a palace. The torches set in holders up and down the corridors smoked and dripped wax which nobody bothered to sweep up. The small, leaded windows were all closed against the fog outside.

At last she reached the room where the waiting women were stitching costumes for the Pageant-Masque. She laid her sketch on the table. Her governess, Lady Frances Villiers, sat there directing operations. Lady Frances had a calm, kind face and kept order extremely well. She glanced at the colored sketch.

"Calisto in blue and pale pink? I shall show the colors to the silk mercers, who come tomorrow. Just now we work on the costume for the Goddess Diana. The gentlemen must arrange their own clothes."

Mary smiled. "My cousin Monmouth will look magnificent. He always does."

She expected her governess to smile, too, but Lady Frances only said thoughtfully, "Why not? At any rate he must appear, or the King will be greatly disappointed."

Anne was a slow little person to coach. She took long to memorize, but she never forgot. She looked forward to the Masque almost more than anyone. Although she loved her sister there was, too, a feeling of jealousy at the back of her heart. Mary did everything better than she did! Mary was clever and quick, and slim and pretty. Anne knew she was none of those things. More than all that. Everyone knew that after their father, Mary was heiress to the throne of Great Britain, so people all paid her great attention.

Though all that would change the moment Father's new wife gave him a son and heir. . . .

But Anne didn't often bother to think things out like that. After all, she was only ten and a half. And yet, little girls grew up quickly in the atmosphere of a court—especially King Charles's Court. They did not often see their ugly, charming Uncle King, for Lady Frances kept them apart from all court festivities as much as possible. Indeed she sighed for the quiet and seclusion of Richmond, and longed for spring to come so that she could take her flock back to safety.

Only sometimes, as the girls sat at their lessons, they would hear a scampering and a barking. Then they glanced at each other over their books. The King's toy spaniels were racing each other along the corridor outside. And perhaps a drawling voice, perhaps a rustle of silks, told them that the dogs' master was somewhere near.

Now, however, lessons were suspended. The King took sudden whims. He had the whim to entertain his new young sister-in-law; to show her that England could stage fine spectacles just as her native Italy did. And it suited his lazy humor to have part of the spectacle performed by his young nieces and their friends.

It was now nearly the end of January. Outside, the snow lay on the narrow streets of London. Poverty and hunger crept down its alleyways, so that sometimes, when the refuse carts made their rounds, they would find a human figure, dead with the cold, propped against the gatepost of a house in whose shadow it had crept for shelter. The bakers did a roaring trade in hot meat pies. The woolen merchants, the silk and velvet sellers, the jewelers, went more often than usual to St. James's Palace and sold more than usual because of all the fine costumes, the swords and helmets and tinsel, to be used in the King's Masque of Calisto.

Darkness fell about four o'clock in the afternoon. After that, the windows of the palace blazed with lights. Music filled the great rooms, rehearsal music played on virginals with painted lids, or on lutes and violins, or sung by the Princess Mary who had the principal part and who, everyone said, sang divinely. But the music died as it flung itself against the cold glass of the windows. Everything outside of the palace was cold and dark.

Yet a small rumor had begun to trickle through London, giving at least imaginary warmth by its hope. It started down in the City, where the merchants watched every change of politics, every fortune of war. It caught the ears of the tradesmen, cut off so long from importing delicacies from abroad on account of the war. And it finally reached the humble little houses in the cobbled side streets where sons and husbands had been kidnaped and forced to fight the Dutch instead of staying at home.

The rumor whispered that his Majesty was considering withdrawing from his alliance with France. That he might, any day, join with his nephew William the Prince of Orange, leader of the Protestant forces in Europe.

Chapter
Three

Mary could not remember a time when her country was not at war with Holland. And yet there had been two periods of uneasy peace. During one of them, her cousin William had actually come over to London to visit his uncle. There is no word of Mary and William meeting; probably they did not, for she was only a child then while he was twenty years old.

But he had made a bad impression on the gay Court, and she was bound to have heard all about that. The Prince of Orange had known no home life, no affection, and had learned to distrust most people. Although he was handsome enough, with those fine Stuart features, he was short, and suffered from asthma, so that he coughed a good deal. His uncle Charles could have forgiven him all that if only he could see a joke. But to William of Orange, life was no joking matter.

Born after his father's death, he had immediately been the cause of violent squabbles between his mother, his managing Dutch grandmother, and his country's most prominent statesmen, all arguing as to who should bring him up. He had never known any real affection or home life, for his mother died when he was a boy. And he was only four when Oliver Cromwell, who ruled England then, and who had been making war against Holland, insisted, as the price of peace, that the little boy should lose his inheritance.

Since then, he had spent his life in grimly fighting to get it back. But not selfishly, just for himself. Louis XIV of France had flooded The Netherlands with his troops, and William wanted to free his people. His uncle, Charles (who had made a secret pact with France behind his nephew's back), tried in vain to get William to give up the struggle. His actual words have come down to us.

"I wish, Nephew, you would take more pains to look at these things better, and not be led by your Dutch blockheads."

But William did not even bother to reply.

That was spoken during a short period of peace between the two countries, when William was over in London. He had been a silent guest, showing nothing but contempt for the rackety goings-on at St. James's. His cold air froze the company and cast a shadow across all their fun. Perhaps he already knew that his uncle had double-crossed him. Certainly he distrusted him, and he did not trouble to hide it. Even the suggested promise of the hand of one of the two little York princesses one day, did not win him over. He merely said he was too busy to think of marriage, and refused the bait.

When he went back to Holland, everyone sighed with relief.

But William forgot this court interlude very quickly. His country was once more in deadly peril. The English had now joined up with the French against him. The Dutch were battling desperately, not just for their land, but for the right to choose their own religion and to govern themselves. That right had once before been taken from them by the Spanish. They knew already what it was to be slaves under a conqueror.

William was a brilliant soldier and a wonderful leader. Young as he was, he planned each campaign which set free yet another corner of his country that had been overrun by French troops. If need be, he said he would even open the dikes and let the sea overrun Holland rather than let the French have it. It was he who first coined that phrase about dying in the last ditch.

His best weapon was the powerful Dutch navy. Those huge ships had come within sight of the English coast more than once. The sound of their bombardment had made England tremble and curse the name of William of Orange. From a little girl Mary had learned to fear him too. To fear him and to laugh at him as well. When Uncle King was feeling merry, he would imitate his gauche and awkward nephew, putting on a thick Dutch accent which made his courtiers scream with laughter.

But Mary had forgotten her cousin in the excitement of preparing for Calisto. She and Anne had grown to love their gentle Italian stepmother, and it was to be in honor of her. Six professional actors and actresses were engaged to help to make it a success. But of course Mary and Anne must naturally have the chief parts!

"And how the dances are to be arranged, I can't conceive!" moaned Mr. Crowne, the Pageant Master—"Little Starch Johnny Crowne" as everyone called him because of the great starched collars he wore. Johnny Crowne hadn't much hair left, and he was almost tearing out what he had.

Mary tried to soothe him. "My cousin Monmouth is the very best dancer at Court. The best dancer in England!" she added with proud loyalty.

"Aye, that he is. He could make his fortune on the stage. But who's good enough to dance with him? With all due respect to your Highness and her friends—no one."

"Sarah—she's good. Sarah Jennings."

Johnny Crowne shook his head. "Not good enough. But don't tell her I said so or she'd scratch my eyes out."

"Poor little Starch!" The lazy, charming tones of James Monmouth sounded behind them. "Why on earth should somebody want to scratch out your eyes?"

Mary said in tones of quiet despair, "There isn't anybody good enough to dance with you. And we *must* have you in our Masque!"

Monmouth patted her kindly. "Well, I suppose so or my father the King will be annoyed. He likes me to shine, you know!"

Humming, the tall elegant figure began to dance by itself; half mockingly, arms outstretched and undulating up and down like some ballet dancer, half seriously so that his grace and balance could be admired. "Tralala, tralala! If nobody's fit to dance with me, why shouldn't I dance alone?"

Johnny Crowne watched him with the appreciation of a connoisseur. When the young duke had finally spun on his heel and then dropped on one knee, arms outstretched toward an invisible audience, the Pageant Master clapped his hands.

"Bravo! I see it now! You must indeed dance alone! A *sarabande* perhaps? Or shall I write you a little *scena?*"

"No, no. Too professional. My father would think I hankered after the stage. . . . I know! A minuet. With an invisible partner. The partner all grace and charm because nobody sees her!"

It was an original idea which might, or might not, come off. Anyhow what they both said was true. Mary was not quite practiced enough to partner him, Anne too small, and the other five girls taking part would only be shown up by his expert smoothness.

What nobody suggested was for any of the professionals (themselves expert dancers) to partner Monmouth. That would never do. Etiquette forbade the courtly amateurs and the paid actors and actresses appearing together even in the same scenes. No, Johnny Crowne knew that. The bell on the clock tower had struck the hour fixed for rehearsal. They all hurried out of the room and made for the hall where the Masque was to be held.

Mr. Crowne had bustled already out of sight. As author of the script and stage manager, he made no bones about pushing past the royal cousins to get downstairs first. Monmouth would not hurry. His part, after all, had not yet been written in. Mary, always dazzled by his appearance and charm, walked shyly beside him.

"I shall love to see you dance alone! Even Sarah would not be good enough to partner you. Mr. Crowne was just saying so. But he said I mustn't repeat it."

"Oh I see . . . But I don't believe Miss Sarah Jennings minds one way or another about her part. She's too taken up with Colonel Churchill. Haven't you noticed?"

Mary remembered with a start that Sarah had seemed distrait, absorbed in something else; that at the court balls and parties (which Mary was allowed to attend for the first time that winter) Sarah had generally been dancing with the same man. A hard-bitten soldier much older than herself, reported to be poor and on the make for a fortune. The son of a mere cavalry captain down in the country somewhere. What was the father's name? Sir Wilson—no, Sir Winston—Churchill. . . .

Mary tried to be worldly-wise. She shook her head and said in the same tones her governess would use, "It won't do.

Sarah has no money either. But Colonel Churchill is only on leave. He'll go back to the war soon, I suppose."

"But the war may come to an end any day."

They had almost reached the room with the improvised stage, and Mary heard the music which was her cue. She had run ahead, not listening.

The little bunch of performers stood waiting for her already. The pupils of Lady Frances Villiers stood alone, waiting to begin their sarabande with castanets. Somebody handed a pair to Mary who clicked them softly, then glided forward to make part of the pattern being woven to the tune the orchestra was playing at the other end of the room.

It was January now. The performance would never be ready in time! The following days were a mad scramble, and the old palace resounded to the hammering of carpenters putting up scenery. The king and his friends were at Whitehall. He had promised to keep away until the night itself. The Duke and Duchess of York were out of London for the moment. This wonderful performance (if it came off successfully) was to greet them—especially the pretty young duchess—when they came back.

Outside, a cold wind swept over Europe. The troops, spread about the Low Countries in frozen billets, waited for word of what was to happen next. Even those who had made the war had tired of it at last. Perhaps a few soldiers of fortune like John Churchill, might regret the coming of peace which would rob them of their opportunities. But the weary, haggard foot soldiers who had been marched and countermarched over icy ground, longed for peace and the chance of going back to their homes.

None of this seemed to penetrate the dark old palace where the girls scampered down passages, shrieking with laughter at the sight of themselves dressed as gods and goddesses. The professional actors strode about majestically in their newly made armor, their cardboard helmets heavy with plumes. Jove, Achilles, the rest of them, playing at what the real soldiers were spilling their blood for, away by the dikes of Holland and the fields of France.

It was indeed a staged masque, set against the bitter reality.

Anne, usually phlegmatic, was not only excited by the thought of her own part, but by the fear that her dearest, divine Sarah might not have the success she should. Sarah was different somehow. She had become very grown-up. It seemed as if she had little time to play games with Anne any more. It was always "Run away, child!" nowadays.

Anne humbly considered it all quite natural. After all, what did it matter, being a princess and royal, if one were only ten and a half and too fat? Sarah was almost fifteen now. Fifteen was grown-up at the Court of King Charles II. Sarah dressed like the court ladies now, and carried a fan.

Naturally she would prefer to spend her time with a handsome officer like Colonel Churchill.

Mary, at least, was old enough, and intelligent enough, to know why so brilliant a soldier as Churchill was back from the wars and hanging about doing nothing. But

Mary's mind was full of the Masque. The rumor about peace being declared hardened and spread. Men said in the streets of London that the negotiations were proceeding now. Merchants down in the City suspended their own money transactions until they saw which way things would go.

And meanwhile, envoys went busily between the magnificent, stately Court of Louis XIV who at one time had conquered nearly the whole of Europe; the raffish, glittering Court of Charles II, who had already sold his country by secret treaty and now wished himself out of the bargain; and William, Prince of Orange, who had had to fight so desperately for existence he hadn't had time to set up a court at all.

On February 9, 1675, England signed the Treaty of Peace with Holland and Spain. France alone remained grimly on the battlefield; but the Prince of Orange now had only one enemy to face. It seemed a miracle that a small country like Holland, led by a young and delicate man, should have withstood the might of France with all its resources of wealth and highly trained troops.

But while France was fighting for conquest and glory, Holland was fighting for her very existence. She had the twin weapons of desperation and in William a leader of military genius. That was what gave the Dutch their miracle advantage.

Mary had forgotten her cousin's warning already. Inside St. James's Palace they scarcely noticed the peace. Everyone was far too occupied in getting word perfect for the

Masque to honor Mary Beatrice of York. They still practiced their dance steps along the passageways, across the
great rooms, without music if need be, because the musicians had gone on strike for more regular hours and refused
to be at the beck and call of everyone any longer.

When the great day came, the palace was astir very
early. Maidservants and pages began to scurry about while
it was still black-dark outside. They brought hot chocolate
to their masters and mistresses and then helped to dress
them. The final rehearsal lasted all morning. Then came a
quickly eaten meal of cold chicken and fruit. Then the
flurry of setting the scenery. Shouts and instructions
echoed through the long hall where the stage was set up.
Somebody tested the pull of the crimson velvet curtains,
lest by any mischance they stuck when lifted to reveal the
first scene. The musicians (meeker, now that it was almost
time to play before His Majesty) set up their desks in
position. And Johnny Crowne, in a freshly starched lace
collar as wide as a baby's bib, spun around and around
like a top, asking questions of this person, answering another.

The King was due to arrive from Whitehall Palace at
dusk. And dusk was falling already.

Suddenly trumpets sounded, blowing a welcome outside
in the courtyard. Mary and Anne were watching at a window near the front entrance. The darkling sky was lit by
the flare of torches carried by running footmen. The
King's own carriage lurched to a stop by the entrance.
Anne giggled and pointed at the spaniel staring back at

her from the carriage window. The King's hand—a fine white hand with a diamond on its forefinger—showed, playing with his favorite's silky long ears.

The King's greatly loved son, the Duke of Monmouth, stepped forward to greet his Majesty and was clapped affectionately on the shoulder. Then . . .

"Quickly, Anne!" Mary caught at her sister's hand and ran out to greet Uncle King in their turn.

The girls curtseyed very low; felt a kindly hand pulling their curls; rose up straight from the curtsey to see their father, who had descended from the next carriage, leading in his sixteen-year-old Italian wife.

They would have curtseyed again, but Mary Beatrice, with the warmth of her Italian blood, held out her arms. Anne threw herself into them. Mary remembered to sketch a reverence to both her parents, before flinging her own arms around the lovely laughing girl who looked so little older than herself.

She greeted her father more timidly. She wanted to love him too, but his melancholy, severe face froze both his children. They saw so little of him. And they had been brought up to consider that the greatest calamity for England would be to have a Catholic ruler.

The chattering, laughing audience swept into the Hall. Candles floating in saucers of water outlined the foot of the huge red velvet curtains which parted slowly to reveal the first scene. More lighting on the stage showed a rocky landscape on whose crags stood poised the nymphs. The

music struck up. Anne advanced waveringly, leading
them, clicking castanets in her pudgy hands. In the midst
of the dance they parted, three to one side, three to another and looked toward where Calisto appeared, graceful
and lovelier than the rest.

Mary began her slow dance. Halfway through she gave a
start and stopped in apparent alarm as she had been
taught to do. She made a sign to the attendant nymphs
and all withdrew, just in time. A company of shepherds
bounded onto the stage and began a hearty, thumping
dance. The King laughed, still stroking the ear of his favorite dog.

Mary stood waiting behind the scenes. Soon it would be
her turn to go on again. Then the Goddess Diana would
appear and rescue her from the shepherds. But where was
the Goddess Diana, who should be holding herself in
readiness to follow her onto the stage?

Mary went in search of her. She found Sarah, in her
goddess' robes with the crescent moon of Diana the Hunt-
ress, talking earnestly in the passage with Colonel Churchill, who should not have been behind the scenes at all.

Mary's usual calmness vanished. She felt indignant that
the entertainment, to which they had all given such
thought should be taken so lightly. She turned to Colonel
Churchill saying coldly, "Here is reserved for the company, sir. Perhaps Miss Jennings did not tell you. Will you
kindly withdraw and join the audience?"

The soldier bowed deeply and walked away. But Mary
had seen a look of amused mockery in his eyes. Sarah,
however, was not amused. She intercepted Mary who was

about to go back toward the stage. She was in one of her rages. Mary saw that at once.

"What harm were we doing?" Sarah cried in a loud, harsh voice.

"You might have been late for your entry."

"Might have been! And you spoke to a fine soldier as if he were a private! As if . . . You *ordered* him to retire!"

The two girls faced each other, their draperies stirring in the draft of the corridor. A lamp caught the paste moon in Sarah's hair. It quivered and sparked as she tossed her head furiously.

Mary forced herself to remain calm. She had never liked this girl. Had distrusted the power she had over Anne. Mary spoke coldly, drawing herself up. "I think, Mistress Jennings, you forget who I am."

"I know very well who you are. A pawn to be wagered on anything the King chooses! Bait held out to the Prince of Orange to persuade him to sign peace with us!"

Mary stopped breathing. She felt a singing in her ears. "How—dare you! That is a lie!"

Sarah shook her red-gold head mockingly. "*I* can marry anyone I like—even John Churchill if I love him enough. (But I haven't made up my mind yet.) You are royal, and may be Queen of England one day. Love can never enter into it with you. You must do as you're told!"

Somebody was coming along the passage toward them; someone who spoke in a clear, calming voice. It was their Governess, Lady Frances Villiers, and Lady Frances had seen enough of her pupils to know when they were quarreling.

"Your Highness! Mistress Jennings! Don't waste time gossiping here. Away with you to the wings and listen for your cue!"

Mary scarcely heard her own cue when it came. She was in a dream. Mechanically she stepped onto the stage and spoke her lines. Mechanically she knelt before Diana, imploring the Goddess to save her from Jove who had tried to capture her and take her away. Was this really to be her fate? Could her kind, laughing uncle, down there in the audience, hand her over like a toy to a cousin hated, feared and unknown?

She would fling herself on her knees before her father; before her kind, loving little stepmother. She would refuse to do as she was ordered! Suddenly she realized the appositeness of the lines she was about to utter. Meaning came into her tones. She flung them defiantly over the footlights, toward the gilded chairs and the dim figures her shortsighted eyes could only see as blurs:

> *"Not that my hate alone on Jove does fall;*
> *But I disdain, and hate to love at all."*

Something of her passion had made the formal thing come to life for the moment. There was a round of clapping. Then Jove's helmet cast its shadow over the rocks behind her and she fled, as the script demanded. But she was hardly conscious of anything more in the Masque until it was the turn of her cousin Monmouth to dance alone.

He had refused to be decked out ridiculously like a god or a shepherd. He wore a court suit of embroidered satin, and across his breast was the ribbon of the Order of the Garter. The George, the badge of the order, swung from his neck as he danced. It caught the eyes of his father the King who had given it to him because it was Charles's most precious possession, and Charles loved his son more than he loved anyone else in the world.

It was the badge which Monmouth's grandfather, Charles the First, had worn on the scaffold at Whitehall long ago.

This was far the best performance of the evening. Johnny Crowne had placed it near the end because he knew it would be so. When the Duke had finished his dance he came forward and bowed low, first to his father, and then to the guest of honor. And the guest of honor clapped her hands with delight, forgetting to speak English, and called out, *"Che bello! O belliss-imo!"* And he bowed again in acknowledgement and kissed his hand to her.

Then the curtain came down. Footmen relit the torches and lamps, and everything was light again. The supper was splendid and gay. But Lady Frances only allowed her charges to sample it, to take a little fruit with them, and then drove them off to bed.

The King's supper parties usually degenerated into rowdiness and horseplay. She would have none of that for her pupils.

Anne, exhausted, fell asleep at once without even finishing the bunch of purple grapes she had taken upstairs with her. But Mary could not sleep. She got out of bed and looked through the parted curtains toward St. James's Park. The night sky was blazing with fireworks, shooting stars, golden rain, everything. . . .

London was celebrating the Peace.

 Chapter
Four

The spring of 1676, more than a year later.

A spring sky, washed in pale blue rises above the Dutch Palace of Honselaarsdijk. The pale red of the bricks seems to warm the sky above, and the gilded balconies under each window glitter in the morning sun. It is a clean, fresh empty landscape, as unlike the darkness and dirt of London as possible. But the State Rooms are empty, too. For the owner of the Palace has no time or use for the sort of crowded entertainment enjoyed by his uncle over in England.

He is walking outside in the garden. A thin, short, unromantic figure with a sensitive face and fine eyes, the

effect almost destroyed by a large hooknose. By his side
walks the English Ambassador to Holland, Sir William
Temple. Sir William's bulk would make two of the
Prince. But he is equally grave, and his middle-aged wis-
dom has won the respect and the liking of William of
Orange.

Perhaps that is why King Charles has sent Sir William
to sound the Prince on such a delicate matter.

The Ambassador had already mentioned the project to
William. Now he paced by his side in silence, not hurrying, not pressing for an answer. It was Temple who had
warned the English Cabinet never to seem in a hurry
when dealing with the Dutch. His words were: "Holland
is a country where the fruit ripens slowly and cannot be
preserved green."

So it was William who, in the end, spoke first. "I am
always being pressed to marry." He spoke shortly as
though anxious to finish with a boring subject. "But as
you know, up till now, it has been quite impossible. I have
been too busy fighting. I have no time."

"As your Highness says, up till now." Sir William allowed himself this much. Then he fell into silence
again.

William had expected him to press and urge like the
others. But the wise statesman knew better. At last the
Prince said rather pettishly, "I know it is a thing to be
done some time or other. And I would rather marry an
Englishwoman than a German. But . . ."

"But, Your Highness?"

The young man by his side began to walk more slowly. Some particular point was making him undecided. The Ambassador sensed this and felt a faint surprise. In battle and in politics he had never known the Prince of Orange hesitate. It was this power of rapid decision which, up to now, had given him the advantage, again and again. Sir William could not imagine what William could be undecided about.

Either one wanted to marry the Heiress of England or one did not.

They had been pacing a stone terrace with a drop to flower beds beneath. William stopped, leaned his elbows on the coping stone of the terrace and appeared to be studying the carpet of tulips beneath him. If he allowed himself leisure for a hobby, it would have been gardening. A love of that, of architecture and of many other beautiful things, were the legacy from his Stuart mother. But for these things too, he had had no time as yet.

"A fine display." The Ambassador looked over the parapet, too, and, equally, seemed to admire the flame-colored mass beneath them. "The *Tulipa Armeniaca*, I think?"

"Sir William"—the young man turned abruptly to him—"may I ask you a question, not as speaking to England's representative, but as to a—a friend?"

Sir William was touched. "Ask what you like. I shall answer you as a friend."

"What is my cousin Mary like?"

Sir William was startled. Royal marriages were affairs of

state. If the Prince had asked the amount of the dowry promised with his bride, or had inquired about his own position, should Mary really succeed to the throne. . . .

But to ask what she was *like*. . . .

"I have not seen her myself." Sir William was cautious. "But I hear on all hands that she is exceedingly beautiful. Perhaps somewhat on the tall side to suit your Highness' own—er—height. Dark hair and eyes, but not swarthy like her uncle. Indeed I have heard that her complexion——"

"A fig for her complexion!" William's air of cold indifference broke down suddenly. "I know her appearance. You forgot that you yourself brought me over her picture to see. No, I meant, what would she be like to live with?"

The Ambassador was more startled than ever. Indeed, it just crossed his mind that the long military campaign had tended to unsettle the Prince and make him eccentric. Royal matches in his day were made quite irrespective of whether the parties even liked each other or not. They were not asked.

While he was wondering how to reply, William began to speak once more.

"Beauty is no criterion of good nature. I do not intend to make a mere formal marriage and then ignore my spouse as—as your master in England has done. But I am engaged in wars enough already. I must have peace at home."

Suddenly the Ambassador understood.

"Her governess, Lady Frances Villiers, is a close friend of my wife's. And women gossip together. What I repeat to your Highness now, is not a mere fabrication in order to bring you more happily to this marriage. According to Lady Temple, it is the truth."

"The truth. Give me the truth!"

"She has all the charm of her great-grandmother, Mary Queen of Scots. But she has more. She has straightforward honesty, and kindness, too."

The Prince drew a quick breath of relief. But still he was not entirely satisfied. "Her temper?"

"Level and equable. That is to say, she is no tame cipher. But she can keep it under control."

William had begun his pacing of the terrace again. He seemed to be turning things over in his mind. The Ambassador watched him sideways, inwardly astonished and amused. Another thing which the Royal Governess had told him, he kept to himself. That the Princess actually looked on her Dutch cousin as a terrible bogy. That she was by no means willing to marry this young man who was considering her so carefully!

But Temple had been sent here to bring about the match if he could. For King Charles now wanted another card to play in his own game against the French. It suited him now to have the Prince of Orange as his nephew-in-law. It gave him some show of reason for offering to negotiate peace between the French and the Dutch. . . .

Sir William said carefully, "Has your Highness considered that you are already one of the heirs to the British throne, but after the Princess Mary? Marry her, and you are one step nearer."

The young face with the hawklike nose turned quickly toward him. "Always supposing the new Duchess of York does not produce a son. In any case, I'm not interested in the English succession. I would rather live and die in Holland."

A passionate love of his own country showed through the words. Again, the Ambassador wondered. This was a most unusual young man!

He went on, feeling his words. "May I take it then, that your Highness is likely to approach the Duke of York for his daughter's hand?"

"You know I am to go over to England sometime. There are matters to be discussed between my uncle the King and myself; matters regarding the peace between our two countries. There will be some opportunity of seeing my cousin then. Afterward, I shall ask for her hand if I am satisfied with what I see."

This time the Ambassador was struck dumb. Never before had any royal prince of the day insisted on inspection first! The Prince understood his silence. Unexpectedly, he burst out laughing.

"Poor Sir William! I know very well what you are thinking. In the great world one acts otherwise. In the great world, one is handed a pig in a poke and supposed to bow and be grateful. But I'm only a plain, rough soldier. I mean first to see what's inside the poke!"

The Ambassador returned to England a few days later with his head in a maze. How was he to convey so insulting a message to the family of the greatest catch in Europe? He broke it first to King Charles, who relieved his mind by bursting into a roar of laughter.

"So he wants to inspect her first? I'll wager no other princess in Christendom has had that compliment paid to her!"

His brother the Duke of York stood beside him looking amazed, then furious. "My daughter's no common milkmaid, to be judged for a new situation! For that, he'll not have her!"

The King turned to him and said pleasantly, "Indeed, she is not. She is my niece and her hand's at my disposal, not yours. Calm yourself, James."

Sir William Temple, alarmed at the Duke's rage, said somewhat anxiously "There is a further stip—message, your Majesty."

"Indeed? Does the Prince *stipulate* any preference for dark or fair?"

The Ambassador moved his feet uncomfortably. "He—he fears that when they meet publicly, she may not be her natural self—may be acting a part. He begs the privilege of catching some glimpse of the Princess unawares."

"The devil he does!" But the angry Duke was waved to silence again by his brother. This was the sort of thing that intrigued Charles. Again he smiled, that slow, charming smile that transformed his dark features.

"Tell him I'll contrive that. . . . Now, James, don't burst like a bottle of wine. Have you not sufficient trust in Mary's beauty and talents?"

Still smiling to himself at the unusual joke, the King

strolled out of the room. At least that young oaf William
showed some originality! And courage, too. For if he refused Mary's hand, the peace between Holland and France
would not be engineered after all. William was not stupid.
He must know that his marriage to the Protestant princess
and heiress was the only card left to play!

Two more summers crept over the London parks. Lady
Frances Villiers took her girls down to Richmond as usual,
to the fine air and freedom, away from the Court gossip
which might have warned Mary what was in store for her.
The three men in the secret said nothing to anyone else. If
Lady Frances suspected that the forthcoming visit of the
Prince of Orange had anything to do with more than poli-
tics, she held her peace.

Let Mary, only fifteen, enjoy her last summer of freedom and, maybe, of happiness too.

But the fruit in the orchard was hardly ripe when they
were told they must return to St. James's. Anne demanded
to know the reason why.

"I don't like London. Nasty dirty place! Dear Lady
Frances, why must we leave so soon?"

The governess thought quickly. Perhaps it was time,
now, to let Mary know what might be before her. "Your
cousin, the Prince of Orange, is coming to London soon.
He will want, naturally, to meet you both."

"Dutch William? We don't want to meet him, do we
Mary?"

Mary felt the same sudden catch at her breath as when
Monmouth had spoken to her that day down by the river.

She dismissed the remembrance fiercely from her mind. William was coming to persuade the King to act as umpire between himself and Louis of France. Nothing more!

But even as she tried to reassure herself, she looked suddenly toward the mirror on the opposite side of the room. The dwarf, Gibson, was reflected in it. His eyes met hers in the glass. And they were pitying.

The Palace of St. James's was being cleaned up in a slapdash manner for the royal visit. Curtains were shaken, floors polished, and the service of gold plate brought from Windsor to embellish the banqueting table. After the banquet there would be a ball. And Mary knew she must dance with William.

She selected the most unbecoming dress she had. Sarah Jennings, who saw it being taken out of its folds, held up her hands in horror.

"That grass-green thing! Your Highness knows how it cheapens you! Now a delicate shade, like your coral gown, or even another shade of green that would show up your complexion instead of killing it dead!"

"Perhaps I want to kill it."

Sarah gave the other a sudden glance of understanding. "Oh, I see——"

"Hush. Here comes Anne."

The Prince had arrived at midday. Anne and Sarah had pressed their noses to a window overlooking the courtyard, watching the royal cavalcade clatter past. But Mary would not look.

"He sits a horse very well. . . . Oh, now he's down, and

what a little man! I thought good soldiers were all fine strapping fellows like Colonel Churchill."

"Be quiet Anne. Don't chatter."

Sarah, half-draped in one of the window curtains, said, "For all that, he has a handsome face. Too big a nose, though."

"How could you possibly see?" Mary asked involuntarily.

"He looked up just now. As if he knew someone was watching him."

Mary was glad she had not gone near the window at all.

The afternoon dragged, for the banquet and ball were not to be until late. The girls old enough to be present grew restive. It was too early yet to begin putting on one's finery, and the wet afternoon left nothing else to do. Anne started to slide on the newly polished floor of the long passage outside their rooms. At first Mary and Sarah disdained to join in. Then they did, trying to swoop and glide in a more dignified fashion, holding their long skirts up, laughing and making almost as much noise as Anne herself while they chased her from one end of the passage to the other. . . .

Suddenly a small silky spaniel darted after them, barking delightedly at the game. The three girls stopped dead. They knew the dog's master could not be far behind. Anne nearly overturned in her curtsey to the King, who appeared at the end of the passage.

"Amusing yourselves?" The rich, lazy voice saluted

them. "Not much room there, though. I tell you what——"
He stopped as if a sudden thought had come to him.
"What about taking your exercise on the ballroom floor?"
   "But it's newly polished!"
   "Aye, that's what I meant. A fine surface, and you'll
only polish it higher." He glanced at their soft heelless
shoes of satin. "Come, lasses. I'll start you off in the first
race. Not Carlo though." He scooped the small spaniel up
under one arm. "You'd scratch the surface with your sharp
nails."
   The girls followed him, Anne giggling. The ballroom
was empty now, prepared for tonight. New wax candles
clustered in the glittering chandeliers swung high above
the floor. They were not lit yet, but sufficient of the pale
London afternoon sun still came through the windows to
illumine the room, all except the Minstrels' Gallery at the
far end which remained in shadow, its crimson curtains
still drawn across the railing in front.
   A thin sound of music stole through the air. The room
was not empty after all. Richard Gibson had stolen in to
play on the painted harpsichord which stood, forgotten, in
one corner. But the dwarf, having dressed himself in his
finery early, had found it and was playing on it, a sad,
melancholy little tune. For he loved music as well as
painting; only few people gave him credit for possessing a
soul.
   Now, seeing the King approach, he sprang up to make
obeisance. The broken tune still echoed throughout the
room. He was dressed in green velvet with silver buttons.

The dog, wriggling free from his master's arm, rushed toward him, nearly knocking him over.

Charles laughed at the dwarf's sudden terror. But Mary stooped down and pulled the spaniel back. The King fished a ball out of one pocket and tossed it across the floor.

"After it, all of you! Gibson too . . ."

The dog raced after it first. Gibson, anxious to obey, slid manfully forward. But the floor was like glass. He suddenly measured his length under the central chandelier. At that, they all laughed. All but Mary who hated to see anyone made a butt and a joke.

"Poor Mr. Gibson! Are you hurt? Here, take my hand."

She raised him gently from his spreadeagled position and started to dust him off with her hands. The little man stood there, red and mortified, his green velvet jacket all crumpled. Anne placed two pudgy hands over her mouth to stifle her laughter. Through her fingers she spluttered, "What a draft you made in your fall Mr. Gibson! See, the gallery curtains have blown apart!"

The King glanced up quickly, almost apprehensively, toward the shrouded gallery above their heads. But the curtains had fallen together again, all but a narrow gap. He shrugged his shoulders, then turned to Mary.

"Perhaps the floor is a trifle slippery for anyone partnerless. . . . Why not some more music instead? Mary, my dear, will you delight us?"

Mary moved slowly toward the harpsichord. She played exquisitely and had a beautiful voice, but today she did not feel like singing. However, the King's wish was a command. She seated herself on the stool before the bright painted lid of the instrument with its garlands of flowers, and laid her hands on the keys. Still, her heart was heavy. She could not sing.

"Well, my dear?" her uncle was saying impatiently.

Mary started hurriedly playing the introduction to the first song which came into her head. Even these few bars soothed her, and when she began the words, written by Herrick, her uncle's favorite poet (maybe that was what had put the song into her head), her voice rang out hauntingly sweet and true:

> *"A heart as soft, a heart as kind,*
> *A heart as sound and free*
> *As in the whole world thou can'st find,*
> *That heart I'll give to thee."*

The King joined in at the next verse, humming the tune under his breath.

> *"Bid me despair, and I'll despair*
> *Under that cypress tree:*
> *Or bid me die, and I will dare*
> *E'en Death, to die for——"*

"Look! It moved again!" Anne's shrill voice broke the spell. She was pointing upward toward the curtains of the Minstrels' Gallery.

The song trembled to silence. Mary took her hands off the keys. The King alone did not look up. He said in a voice louder than usual, " 'Tis only the draft blowing them. They've not heated up the place properly yet. Off you go, girls. Mary I thank you. It would be poor thanks to keep you so that you are too chilled to dance tonight!"

Subdued, they knew not quite why, the girls left the great ballroom and returned to their own quarters in the palace. The clock over the stables chimed the hour. In any case, it was time for Mary and Sarah to put on their finery for tonight. . . .

Anne crept into Mary's room, later, to see her sister in her ball dress. She looked startled and horrified.

"*That* old dress? And—and why are you putting that chalky stuff on your face?"

Mary turned from the dim mirror to face Anne. Gone seemed the lovely girl who had romped on the ballroom floor only a short while ago. All the color and sparkle that had lit up her delicate features while she was singing, was gone; blotted out by the layer of chalk-white powder that made her look like a ghost. Her beautiful jet-black curls were dragged off from her forehead. And she had laden herself with the most unbecoming jewelry she could find.

"You look awful! The Prince won't even dance with you!"

"All the better, my sweet. I don't want him to."

Anne's thoughts were suddenly deflected to something else.

"Mary, listen. I'm sure there was a man watching us up in the gallery!"

It was Mary's turn to look startled. "What nonsense! The wind stirred the curtains. You heard the King say so."

"When we were running along the passage back here, I looked back. I *saw* a man coming down the little staircase from the gallery!"

It was possible that one of the footmen had stolen up there to get a glimpse of Charles romping with his nieces. Mary said so thoughtfully, fingering the ugly necklace which clashed with her dress.

"He should be dismissed." Anne said stoutly. "Spying on us like that! I'll tell Lady Frances."

"Would you know him again?"

"N-no." Anne looked disappointed. "The staircase was dark." Then she remembered something and cheered up. "I saw his shadow on the wall though, when he passed by the light at the bottom. A little shadow with a big hooked nose!"

Chapter
Five

All that night St. James's throbbed to music and laughter. The lights from the palace windows cast yellow squares down on the courtyard beneath. The palace guards stepped back and forth over the squares, rubbing their hands surreptitiously for it was cold outside. But not now, in the ballroom. Great fires had been lit at either end, and the hundreds of fine wax candles, lit too, warmed the air as well as catching the glitter of silks and jewels.

The curtains of the Musicians' Gallery were drawn apart now. The music streamed down from it, syncopated by talk and laughter as each formal dance came to an end. Gossip buzzed through the room. The Prince of Orange

danced well enough after all, though stiffly and without a
smile. Look at Sarah Jennings over there, flirting with
Colonel Churchill as usual! The little Duchess of York was
in great beauty, was she not? But the Princess Mary! No
chance of a match there, judging by her appearance tonight!

"Nonsense, he must marry her! Who ever heard of a prince
judging by appearances!"

"True. But he has never smiled once. And she danced
with him stiff as a poker."

"He lives by policy, not smiles. I'll wager he bores his
Majesty to death!"

Sir William Temple, watching the scene from an anteroom was not deceived. He knew William's impassive face,
so different from the false smiles, the intriguing glances, of
the courtiers about him. Yet even he was surprised when
the Prince of Orange, snatching a moment to step aside
and join him, actually threw his arms round him, embrac-
ing him.

"My dear friend! I believe I am going to be a happy
man after all!"

"You mean—the Princess?"

"She is all and more than you said. Gentle and kind.
And beautiful, too, in spite of her efforts to look otherwise. Tomorrow morning I shall ask the King for her
hand."

"Your Highness, I am delighted." But Sir William was
puzzled as well. Never could he have believed that Princess Mary could have looked otherwise than beautiful. But

tonight! And she had moved through the dance with her cousin like a doll wound up by machinery!"

Then he remembered the King's promise, and a slow smile overspread his own face. Somehow, somewhere since coming to the palace, William had been given his opportunity of seeing Mary as she was.

He only wished he knew how it had been contrived.

He said cautiously, "May I give your Highness a word of advice?"

"You may say anything to me. You are my friend."

"The Princess is young and romantic. She has been brought up to think of you as an ogre. Frankly, your Highness has not done much tonight to disabuse her of that impression!"

William frowned. "You mean, I should have flattered her—paid her compliments? I am not a courtier. I am a soldier."

"If she saw you as you are now, your frankness and warmth, it would do much to win her heart. For it *is* her heart that you want?"

William said gravely, "Yes. She is a woman I could love. But I cannot force her to love me in return. She must learn to know me after we're married."

"No wooing?" The Ambassador suggested slyly.

But William only answered in the same grave tones, "There's no time. The marriage must go through as quickly as possible. I must return quickly to Holland and take her with me."

The Ambassador sighed.

· ❧ ·

Mary slept late that morning. She was awakened by her little maid coming to her in a flurry. "Madam, your father, the Duke, wants to speak to you urgently."

Mary slipped out of bed, combed her black hair hastily and threw a long robe over her shoulders. She went into her sitting room next door and found her father standing there, rapping his nails against the window. The Duke was angry and upset. He had not wished this marriage from the first. He had not wanted his daughter to marry a Protestant. Bad enough that she and her sister had been taken from him to be brought up in the Protestant faith against his will!

So, angry as he was, he broke the news to her harshly, with no show of affection or pity. "William has asked for your hand. The King insists. You must obey."

She stared at him, her face now as white as it had been last night under its coating of powder. So the nightmare was true! And she had slept soundly that night, confident from William's cold courtesy and indifferent manner that she had managed to evade this fate!

Frantic, she fell on her knees and tried to catch at her father's hand. But he drew it away, saying, "No acting, Miss, if you please! You did enough of that last night!"

She searched his face, unbelieving. This was her father! The man who had played with her as a child, who had seemed to love and admire her until they were snatched from each other. Surely he minded that they might never see each other again!

"You are sending me out of England! I'm your daughter. Do you not care?"

A strange look came into the handsome face. Yes, he cared. He had loved both his daughters deeply. But he dared not withstand his brother Charles. And because he wanted no tears and only hoped to bring the scene to a close, he said roughly, "What is the matter with going to Holland? You will live very comfortably there."

She could not believe he had spoken the words. "Not to see you again! Or Anne——"

"Oh, Anne." He shrugged his shoulders. "She may make the journey some day if she will. But I cannot. I am the heir. You must learn that princesses have to stay by the side of their husbands. You should know that by now."

The hard, cruel words cut her to the heart. "Rise up," he said sharply. "See to your trousseau, your packing. You have little enough time."

She gave him one long look as she rose to her feet. It was as if she were saying good-by already. Good-by to the father she had once loved. Good-by to something his words had killed.

Only after she had got back to her bedroom, did the tears come. Then she flung herself on the bed, sobbing uncontrollably. When they brought her food, she refused to touch it. She lay there until it was dark. When somebody scratched gently at the door, she paid no attention at first. Then it struck her that it might be Anne. She called out hoarsely, "Come in!"

Somebody entered, carrying a candle. It was not Anne. It was Mary Beatrice, her stepmother who bent over her, kissing away the tears.

"Mary, I know how hard it is. I went through it myself."

Mary turned her face to the wall.

The kind little Italian sat down on the edge of the bed. "Mary, listen to me! I was affianced to your father without even seeing him. I was not asked, either, whether I wished to marry him or not. And I have grown to love him. Perhaps you, too——"

Mary shook her head violently. She cowered farther under the bedclothes, away from the caressing hand. The other went on, pretending not to notice.

"I know you are grieving at leaving England. I, too, grieved at leaving Italy——"

Mary muttered, "That's a different matter entirely. Italy is not England."

Mary Beatrice smiled sadly to herself. She knew the English character by now. However warmly the sun shone in Italy, no matter how much more beautiful the palaces and gardens there, still, Italy was "foreign." Like Holland. So it was no use talking. She rose again. Suddenly Mary turned toward her, grasping the silk folds of her dress.

"Anne! Where is Anne! Why has she not come to see me—to comfort me?"

There was a pause. Then her stepmother said, "Anne has a—chill, a slight fever. It is better that she does not risk giving it to you."

"She said the ballroom was drafty. She must have caught cold there. Poor Anne!"

Then Mary turned her face to the wall again and said no more.

In the following days, she kept to her room as much as she could. When she had to appear, everyone noticed how her face was blotched with crying. She would not see William alone. When they met at court functions she treated him formally, giving her hand with her head turned away. Sir William Temple was quite perturbed by her unaccustomed rudeness.

"I beg of you to overlook it," he said to the Prince of Orange. "She is almost a child still. It is a child's pique."

"No," said the Prince. "Those tears are the tears of a woman true to her feelings. It is her feelings I must change, and that will take time."

Then the Ambassador saw that William admired Mary all the more for her faithfulness to her country and to her own heart. And a faint hope sprang up that Mary would learn to value the faithfulness and honesty of her new husband, seeing they were unaccustomed virtues at her uncle's court, but virtues she possessed herself.

The night before the wedding, a footman brought a package to Mary's sitting room. She suspected what might be in it, and would not even open it. But Sarah, who was in the room, opened it without permission. The wrappings fell apart to show a silver box of Dutch workmanship. Even Sarah, however, hesitated at opening the box.

"Don't you want to see what's in it?" She fingered the catch.

"No. It will only be a present from *him*."

"But your Highness will have to thank him. And how

can you thank him properly without knowing what it is?"

"Then open it yourself."

Sarah sprang the catch open. In spite of herself, Mary drew nearer to see what the box contained. The sparkle of diamonds, the gleam of rich red rubies, shone in their eyes. It was a magnificent necklace. Sarah lifted it reverently from its velvet bed. "There's a note under it!" she cried.

It was William's handwriting. It paid no compliments, addressed her in no fine language. It merely said, "This was my Mother's necklace. I ask you to value it because it was hers."

Uncle King's sister. She too went to Holland. Protesting and weeping? She had been only twelve years old, Mary remembered. Widowed at nineteen before her only child, William, was born. And living alone in a foreign country without even a husband to support her. She, too, must have spent her days longing for the green of Richmond Forest in summer, and even the smoky air of London in winter. . . .

In these days when journeys were difficult and often took weeks, and when countries were separated from each other by constant wars, princesses who married foreign husbands seldom saw their own countries again.

Sarah said, "*Her* name was Mary Stuart, too. . . ."

The wedding took place by candlelight in a room in the palace. Mary had stood stiffly allowing her maids to deck her out, not caring what dress they chose to put upon her. Only once, when they opened her jewel box, did she show some animation. Putting her hand out to stop them, she opened, instead, the silver box from Holland. She lifted out the ruby and diamond necklace and clasped it around her long, white throat.

"Charming! Enchanting!" The maids chorused. Mary paid no attention. She sailed out of the room, her head held high. Like her ancestress, the first Mary Stuart, she felt she was going to her execution.

Her uncle was in high spirits that evening. He even interrupted the Bishop of London once or twice, during the wedding service. When the Bishop demanded, "Who gives this woman to wife?" Charles said loudly, "I do," taking the words out of his sulky brother's mouth.

William acted stiffly and correctly throughout the ceremony. Mary's hand, stone-cold, was laid in his. When he had to echo the Bishop's words "With all my worldly goods I thee endow" he stepped forward, as was the custom then, and laid a handful of gold and silver coins on the velvet prayer book.

Charles grabbed them and tossed them over to his niece. "Put it in your pocket, 'tis all clear gain," he told her.

William frowned. He considered his uncle's levity misplaced.

As soon as that wedding was over and Mary felt the gold ring on her finger, she looked around the half-dark room, searching for the first person whom she thought would run forward and embrace her. Before the ceremony, she had felt too stunned to notice who was present. Now she peered through the candlelit room.

"Anne? Where is Anne!"

Lady Frances said quickly, "She still has some fever. We thought it best to keep her away."

Mary said nothing. But the tears, barely dry, fell down her white cheeks again. Her hand felt a slight, sympathetic pressure. She snatched it away from William's grasp.

It was November, and desperately cold. But outside, the dark sky was alight with the flame of bonfires, for the Londoners were rejoicing in this wedding which seemed to seal the Protestant Succession and insure that the old days of loss of liberty under the Catholic Queen Mary Tudor would never occur again. Night after night the bonfires were lit and burned through the still air. Then suddenly a downfall of rain and wind blew them out.

The seasons of storms had begun. Charles suggested that the young married couple should stay where they were until it was over. But William was impatient now. He would not hear of it.

"I have a storming bride already," he answered sharply. "I will wait no longer before I take her home." His patience was wearing thin.

 Chapter
Six

They left London on the nineteenth of November,
1677.

The night before Mary's rooms were still in disorder,
trunks standing only half packed. Twenty times she had
changed her mind about what to take, what to leave behind. And still she cried as they carried away her old
schoolbooks, her old toys, long since finished with, but
reminding her of happier days. No, they said to her. Your
Highness cannot burden the ship with such things!

The dwarf Richard Gibson knocked timidly at her
door, then went in carrying something in his two arms. It
was a picture, elaborately framed and almost as tall as

himself. "My wedding present!" he gasped, setting it down on the floor. "I would have given it sooner, but it wasn't finished till yesterday.

Mary wiped her eyes and looked at it. It was a view of Richmond Palace, worked up in oils from a sketch taken the summer before. There stood the palace, half masked by trees, and the cupolas gleaming and the weather vanes glinting with gold.

She threw her arms round the little man in gratitude. Then she said to her attendants, "Quick! Order the carpenter to make a case for this. Whatever else is left behind, it must go with me. I shall treasure it all my life!"

One thing more she was determined about. They were still keeping her from Anne. Nobody seemed to remember that she must say good-by to her sister. When Gibson had gone, she left the room quickly and went along the corridor to Anne's room. Surely a feverish cold was a trifle compared with not saying good-by to Anne!

She tapped on the door. There was no reply. She opened it and stood amazed. The room was empty. The bed, where Anne should have lain, was smooth and empty, too. What had happened?

William stepped quietly into the room behind her. He had gone to speak to her in her own room, and had caught a glimpse of her flying figure. She turned on him.

"Where is Anne? Where is my sister? Something has happened to her!"

William spoke more gently than usual. "Anne has been

very ill. She was moved to another part of the palace. I said you should have been told, but they would not listen. They feared the infection if you insisted upon seeing her."

"The infection?"

"Anne has had smallpox."

She stared at him, speechless and horrified. He said quickly, "She's better, but not well yet. She knows you are going away. Believe me, she grieves as much as you do."

Mary said in a whisper, "You are sure she is—going to get well?"

"I swear it. You can believe my word."

And looking at William, Mary knew that she could. The courtiers—even Lady Frances—might have lied to her. But this man would never lie. For the first time a small feeling of comfort, even of hope, stole into Mary's heart. For the first time she felt that here was someone upon whom in an emergency, she could completely depend.

He was speaking again. "You trust me, Mary? At least you can do that?"

"Yes." She said slowly. "I can trust you—at least."

The royal barge had been moored on the Thames near the palace to take them to where they must embark. Even down the river, the wind blew so strongly, the trees bent their heads as if in farewell to her as she drifted past, away from London, away from everything that she knew. It blew the rain in gusts against the glass panels of the little cabin in which Mary sat. But the bitter rain was no colder than the tears which began to flow as she said good-by to every known landmark, to London Bridge, to the spires of Whitehall, and the old tower of St. Paul's.

William, sitting beside her, had gone into his shell again. He was a stranger once more. He helped her to disembark, then muttered a Dutch expression of annoyance at seeing the cavalcade waiting to say good-by to them at the small town of embarkation on the coast.

There were many coaches that had followed from London by road. The coaches were full of courtiers come to pay their respects to the girl who might one day become their sovereign. One figure alone had ridden all the way on horseback. Mary recognized him with joy.

"My cousin Monmouth! Dear James, so you made the journey to say good-by to me!"

Monmouth dismounted and kissed her hand. He looked handsomer than ever, tall and proud, with the bearing of a king. Beside him, William seemed insignificant. Yet the two men bowed with an odd respect to each other. They had known each other as soldiers, fighting in the Dutch wars. Then, they had been on opposite sides. But that did not matter. Each could appreciate the soldierly qualities of the other.

"Here is someone else, come to bid you good-by!" Monmouth smiled and gestured toward a small figure climbing down from one of the court carriages. "He insisted on coming. They said there was no room, but he offered to sit upon the knees of one of the ladies, or up on the box. As, indeed, I see he has done."

Richard Gibson presented a bedraggled sight. All through the wind and rain he had sat cowering under a cloak now wringing wet. He tried to make a fine gesture with his plumed hat, but the soaked feather dripped down on his face.

"My lady! I couldn't let ye go without another glimpse of that pretty face. I'll be your servant all my life!"

Mary stooped and kissed him. Now it was no longer rain but tears that trickled down the dwarf's face. Monmouth said quickly, "I'll look after him, Mary. He shall be my charge against the horseplay and buffeting you used to protect him from. And when I come over to visit you, I'll bring him with me. I promise you that."

"Promise you'll come?" She gazed up tearfully into his face.

"Of course I'll come. Our cousin William will invite me. Won't you, William?"

William nodded curtly, his eyes on the stormy sea. Far against the horizon he saw the English ship, loaned to take him and his bride home to Holland. He longed to cut short the painful scene.

"Finish your good-bys," he said curtly. "We must get aboard."

The courtiers who heard him, gasped. One of them said "But, your Highness, you must wait till the wind changes!"

William's patience suddenly snapped "I will wait no longer. Wait for more tears? Rather would I risk the storm out there than prolong this storm of emotion!"

Monmouth said coldly, "I have a message from his Majesty. He advises, in this weather, that you return to London and wait till it becomes more favorable. Remember, you have your bride to consider."

Mary suddenly drew herself up to her full, tall height. Before her husband could speak, she said proudly, "I am not afraid of any storm. If I must go, let me go quickly."

She looked every inch a Stuart as she spoke. Then, suddenly she remembered Anne and her new composure almost broke down again. "My sister!" she cried to Monmouth. "How is she? How is Anne?"

Monmouth spoke easily, reassuringly. "Oh, I bring a message from her too. She is much, much better. She ate a good supper last night and sends her fond love."

"Truly?"

"Truly of course."

Mary searched his face, than glanced toward that of her impassive husband. In that flash of interchange she learned something. If William had brought the message, she could have believed it. But Monmouth was too like his father. He was quite capable of making up the bit about the supper—as well as anything else.

Almost with relief she turned to William. "I am ready to go."

They had to embark first in a small yacht with only a bit of covering for Mary to sit under and keep herself as dry as possible from the rain. Her attendants were crammed into the after part of the yacht while another boat followed behind, laden to the gunwales with baggage.

As soon as the yacht left the shelter of the breakwater it began to toss like a cork. Mary suddenly felt her husband's arm around her, holding her stiff in a brace, protecting her from damage against the side of the boat. She twisted round to get a last glimpse of the harbor. It seemed to toss up and down too like a gray ball thrown in the air, while the carriages grew smaller and smaller until they appeared like toys, drawn up by the pier.

And there stood her cousin Monmouth, mounted upon his horse again, like a toy officer, one arm, tiny in the distance, waving good-by.

She turned back to face the storm.

A great wall of timber shot up through the mists before her. The ship had been riding the storm outside the harbor. Faces looked down on her from the deck. They let down a rope ladder with a seat, like a cat's cradle, contrived on it. William leaned forward and steadied the seat against the side of the yacht.

"Climb in," he ordered. " 'Tis perfectly safe."

For that sort of thing, Mary had courage enough. She got herself into the seat which swayed perilously upward. Now she had reached the deck. Rough hands grabbed her and drew her on board. The rope-seat went down again for her ladies. She heard some of them squealing with terror. . . .

William's voice sounded behind her. "Get down to the cabin below."

It was the captain's own cabin, specially decorated for her use. Velvet cushions had been placed on the bunk, but the force of the storm had cast them onto the floor. William picked the cushions up and wedged them about her, seating her between them. Her attendants now crowded into the cabin, some of the ladies crying, all disheveled and wet. But, curiously, it was William's arm that she clung to, and missed when it was withdrawn.

"Will you not stay with me?" she asked piteously.

He shook his head, though his eyes were kind. "We are about to cast off. My place is on the bridge with the captain. You would not have me cower down here like a woman?"

When he had gone, she turned around in her wedged seat and tried to look through the one porthole left uncovered. She heard the clang of the anchors being lifted, felt the sudden lurch and straining of timbers as the great ship swung her head east. She must get one last look at England!

But only a curtain of mist met her eyes.

The horrible journey took the whole night. All her ladies were seasick but Mary was not. All night she sat upright among her cushions, too proud to give in to either weather or grief. Sometimes the ship mounted a great wave, hovered on its pinnacle and then rushed down the other side, to settle again, trembling. But Mary was beyond caring. If she died, she died.

Then, as a pale gray dawn crept through the porthole, it seemed to her as though they were going more steadily. They had reached the lee of the land. The sky became a washed-out winter blue. The ship tacked about, and now

she could see the approaching coast: a long white line of
sand dunes, a few huddled cottages and one gaunt wind-
mill throwing its arms against the sky. . . .

William came hurriedly down into the cabin. "We
should have sailed right up the Maas into The Hague, but
ice floes prevented. We are landing at Terheyde instead."

"Terheyde?"

"A fishing village only a few miles off." He spoke impatiently. "Can you compose yourself, Mary? Smile, even,
though I know you don't feel like smiling. But the people
from miles around are gathered already to greet you. I can
see quite a crowd on shore."

When she got on deck she saw them too. A patient line
of humble people, fishermen and their families, standing
there in the cold, as impassive as William himself. She had
already combed her hair, sponged her face in scented
water. One of her maids threw around her shoulders a dry
cape with a little white ermine collar and hood. The wind
had whipped color into her cheeks. She was swung down
the side of the great ship by the rope ladder and, seating
herself in the waiting yacht, prepared herself for her first
entry into her husband's country.

He sat down beside her. He shaded his eyes to look
toward a cluster of figures standing at the edge of the
landing stage. He said anxiously, "I think it is the local
burgomaster with a deputation, come to greet you. It—it
would be nice if you could return his speech with a few
words of Dutch. Could you manage it, Mary, if I taught
you now?"

"What, now?"

"Just a few words. It would gratify them." His voice was almost pleading. "Say after me, *'Dank U, goede lieden.'* It means 'Thank you, good people.' Short, but enough."

The ridiculousness of learning Dutch in this cockleshell of a boat actually brought a smile to her lips. He saw the dimples come and then disappear. Her first lesson in Dutch! Well, she had better begin now, for there had been no time for lessons before she left home.

"Dank U, goede lieden," she murmured, gathering her skirts together, ready to disembark.

The small yacht was drawing alongside the pier. William stepped out first, giving his hand to Mary. The fisherman-mayor of the town advanced, a piece of written paper in his hand. He began to read from it, his rough, hoarse voice making the guttural Dutch sound even uglier than it was. Mary listened politely. From the glances and bows in her direction she guessed that it was a speech of welcome. Suddenly, she was touched by those plain people who were greeting her as well as they could. When the man had run down and was standing awkwardly before her, she gave him her enchanting smile. Then she made a low curtsey to them all and said her little phrase of Dutch as loudly and clearly as she could.

Instantly, everyone smiled in return. William gave her a light pat of approbation. Her heart warmed in spite of herself. She felt the villagers' admiring glances as she walked forward to the carriage hastily summoned to take them inland.

There were only a few bent, twisted trees to break the monotony of the road winding over the dunes. Everywhere the frozen earth was scored by canals running down to the sea, canals reflecting the color of the sky above. Yet Mary felt suddenly content. Her despair had lifted a little because she had taken her first step in this strange land gracefully and well, and she knew it.

It was a long drive. They passed through villages where the people stood patiently to catch a glimpse of their new princess, and once more she managed to smile and wave to them. She felt William was approving of her, proud of her even. Only a short while ago she would not have cared. Now, somehow, she did.

Gradually, the land was becoming more civilized. A long stone wall appeared, pierced by a noble gateway. Through it she glimpsed the façade of the Palace of Honselaarsdijk, where they were to have a few days' rest before their triumphal entry into The Hague. It looked very different now, from that spring morning when William had walked in the garden with Sir William Temple. Today the gilded balconies were powdered with snow. The flower beds were only white mounds. Yet it would always appear magnificent and stately, winter or summer.

Once inside, Mary stared about her in amazement and pleasure. The whole place smelled clean!

She had a passion for cleanliness, and had always subconsciously hated the stuffy odors in her uncle's palaces. Here, the clear morning light shone on parquet floors without a speck of dust on them. The furniture was as grand as at home, but it looked better kept. The gilding glittered instead of looking peeled and scratched. The damask upholstery on the chairs was fresh and unstained. In her own apartments, the windows were draped with deliciously patterned Indian cottons brought from the East through the Dutch East India Company. Here were no fusty velvets, hanging with germs and dust!

The greatest wonder of all opened off her own bedroom. This was a bathroom, the first she had ever seen. Nowhere else in Europe except Holland could such a thing be found. Not with taps to turn on the water and drainage to take it away. The taps were made in the shape of swans' heads and were of pure silver. She twisted one of them around. Instantly a gush of water spouted from its beak into the marble bath. It was a miracle.

When she stepped back into her room again, William was waiting for her. "You like your apartments?"

"They are—beautiful. More beautiful than anything at home."

He looked pleased. "When summer comes, you will enjoy the scent of the roses under your window. I planted new ones there last year."

"You are fond of gardening?" There seemed so much to learn about the tastes of this strange man.

"If I had been free to study some other subject besides war, I would have chosen botany. Or perhaps architecture. I like to create things of beauty."

You? She almost exclaimed with astonishment. Then

she looked into his eyes, the only handsome part of him. They were sad Stuart eyes. Of course all the Stuarts loved beauty! Only this one had enough strength of character to curb his tastes and attend to urgent necessities first. . . .

The palace was warmed from end to end by great porcelain stoves. No more draughty corridors or scorching fires that scorched when one came near and left one shivering as soon as a step was taken away from them. Beautiful Oriental porcelain adorned the shelves, and every day Mary found something more to admire.

She looked long at the portrait of William's father and mother; they looked back at her from the painted canvas, brave in silks and satins, just a boy and a girl, hand in hand. The girl had William's eyes. Child as she seemed, she appeared to be pleading with Mary: Look after my son!

Day after day state coaches lumbered out from The Hague, filled with prominent people come to pay their respects. Mary noticed that the men stuck to sober black, though it might be velvet adorned with silver or diamond buttons and buckles. They did not wear the gaudy colors fashionable at her uncle's court. The women were mostly large and high-colored. Mary had her first lesson in Dutch etiquette when it came to dealing with them.

"You must kiss the ladies of the aristocracy, but give your hand only, to the wives of officials," William told her.

It was simple to know which was which, for the Court Chamberlain announced the name and rank of each lady as she came forward to be presented. But they all wanted to be treated as aristocrats and were counting on Mary's ignorance of their court customs. And there is a certain obstinacy about the Dutch character which, well directed, accounted for their success in maintaining their freedom. Mary was to learn this through seeing it less admirably displayed.

The first lady to enter the audience room was the wife of a minor official. She was splendid in crimson velvet, and as she swept forward she made a decided peck toward Mary's cheek.

Mary drew back, then held out her hand with a sweet and friendly smile. The peck landed in the air. Greatly affronted, the lady withdrew, but she was not the only one to try this maneuver. Mary circumvented them all, leaning her own soft cheek toward the persons privileged to receive her kiss, and allowing only her hand to be kissed by the others.

She had obeyed William. But it seemed such a little thing, and so easy to give pleasure if one was allowed to do so! William disagreed. She had acted perfectly. "One must have discipline at court as well as in the field," he told her.

Fortunately the court language was French, and Mary spoke French very well. So did William, with none of the heavy accent which spoiled his English in spite of having an English mother. But Dutch had to be learned too and she must begin lessons with a tutor as soon as the ceremony of entering The Hague was over. It would be like beginning her lessons at Richmond once more!

On December 14, they drove into the old capital in a

coach drawn by six horses. Crowds skated down the canals keeping level with the speed of the coach. It was a whirling landscape of snow and swiftly gliding figures. When they approached the city, the bells rang out, vibrating the still air so that one might almost imagine the sound reaching as far as the coast.

And the crowds went cheering mad. They cheered Mary for her grace and beauty, but Mary herself knew that the real enthusiasm was not, as yet, for her but for her husband. There was almost an air of worship as they waved toward him and threw their hats in the air. She had already learned a few words of Dutch. She understood two of the words they continually called out toward William's side of the carriage.

"Our savior! Our Prince!"

And the still, small figure beside her scarcely made any response, only lifted his hand now and then. A sort of awe fell upon her as she bowed and smiled through the glass. All this for the man her uncle and his court laughed at and despised! She wondered, that instant, if she could possibly have misjudged him, too. He had sacrificed every comfort, risked life itself, for his people. They knew it. Tonight had shown her the first faint glimmer of that sacrifice.

After dark there was a great display of fireworks. Mary and her husband watched them from the balcony of their town palace, The Binnenhof. Far down below them, the river Vijver ran like a black serpent through the lighted streets. The crowds massed along its banks, only the flaring torchlight illumining a white disk of a face here and there or, suddenly, the color of a cloak.

Mary's own cloak was of sable. Standing out there on the balcony, she scarcely felt the cold for an inner excitement which warmed her as well. She watched the fiery wheels circle above her; the golden rain fall, quenched, into the blackness below. The display ended in a wonderful set piece showing St. George slaying the Dragon, which she knew to be meant as a compliment to her English blood. It drew gasps of awe from the crowds. But they cheered only when letters of fire scrawled across the sky the proud motto of the House of Orange:

MOI, JE MAINTIENDRAI.

There had been a moment's pause while people spelled out the words. Then, as the letters began to fade, a roar came from the crowd, cheering madly the slim figure standing on the balcony with his fur-clad bride beside him. Indeed, he had maintained his nation, winning their freedom by his own courage and brilliance.

Mary was startled. She had heard cheering often enough before. But it had been the lighthearted cheering of the London crowd at a spectacle. Never had she heard this note of gratitude before. As she listened to it, a small spark of something like pride in her husband awoke in her heart.

"Come." He touched her lightly on the arm. "We have shown ourselves to them long enough."

The motto trembled away into the dark. It was dark enough during the long drive home, away from the torches and flares of the city. William was always silent, but this time Mary sat silent, too. What had happened to her? Her emotions were so confused, she had actually forgotten for a whole evening her dread of this strange husband sitting by her side. . . .

He was coughing. She remembered suddenly his weak chest; how he had stood out there in the cold with no cloak to hide his soldier's uniform and the bright ribbon of the House of Orange across his breast. They were little dry coughs which seemed to choke him. Alarmed, she exclaimed, "You are chilled! Here, take my cloak——"

In the throes of one of his fits of asthma, he could not protest. She wrapped the warm furs about him. When he recovered a little, he fumbled in one of his pockets and drew out a small phial, which he held to his nose. The essence it contained seemed to revive him. She watched him anxiously.

"It is nothing. It is all over." He tried to reassure her. "This comes on me often enough."

She saw he desired no fuss, so she sat silent again. Now the landscape began to glimmer whitely, overlaid with snow. The gates of the Palace of Honselaarsdijk came into sight at last. Once inside the palace, the warm air from the stoves revived them both. William even laughed a little as he snatched off her cape from his shoulders before any of his attendants could see him in such effeminate dress. And she laughed back, out of sheer relief.

Then she ran toward her own beautiful bathroom, where sleepy maids stood ready to undress her, and with her own hands turned on the silver taps.

 Chapter
Seven

When spring came, a carpet of tulips flowered under her window before the roses were even in bud.

William might like roses best, but tulips were the best-loved flowers of the Dutch. He taught her the names of them; showed her the small Tulip of Constantinople; the broad leaves of the Tulip of Candy which flowered either red or white. They bore such enchanting names!

She walked down the long terrace with William while he called upon her to admire the tulips which bore two shades as if one color, damped by the rain, had run into the other. Some of them had fringed petals, too. Those were the ones most thought of in Holland; the ones whose bulbs cost most money to buy. And while she admired obediently, she wondered. She was amazed once more that this cold, silent man by her side should suddenly show such a knowledge of flowers.

Again she had caught a glimpse of the other side of his character. Hidden deep down was his passionate love of beauty.

"Tulip." She echoed softly, adding, "Such a strange name!"

"The name comes from Tulpan, where our traders first found the bulbs, grown by Turks in the east," he explained.

"I thought your traders only brought back things to eat!" She ventured to tease a little, and was glad to see him smile.

"Some people tried to eat the bulbs, so the joke goes. They do resemble onions a little." The smile vanished. "But then came the craze for speculating in them. That was long ago, in my father's day. Everyone bought or sold rights in a new rarity. Fantastic prices were asked for them. The poor people invested their savings with dishonest dealers who did not even have bulbs to sell . . . until the crash came."

Her kind spirit leaped to the real tragedy of that. "You mean, the poor people lost all they had?"

He nodded. "In Haarlem especially. Haarlem was the center of the speculative boom. The governors of the city had to announce that all deals since last planting time were canceled, which brought the trade to a standstill.

Thousands were ruined, rich merchants and poor alike. It has taken forty years for the city to recover."

He stopped abruptly in front of a bed of the great Semper Augustus tulip. "Haarlem should have a state visit! That would still more encourage trade. You shall go and enchant them my dear."

He had emphasized the "you." She said anxiously, "Not alone, surely!"

But he gave a short, quick nod, saying, "The French are massing along our borders again. I had another dispatch half an hour ago." He laid his hand lightly on her shoulder. "It is fortunate that I leave so charming an ambassadress behind. You always do and say the right thing, Mary."

"In my bad Dutch?"

"It gets better. But you should not be so entirely surrounded by your English suite. Then you chatter in English, whereas if you had a Dutch dresser——"

Mary's heart sank. After all, she was only sixteen. "I have plenty of Dutch court ladies about me. *Old* ladies who can't see a joke. And so stiff and exact!"

He smiled at her. "Well, never mind. Let us cheer ourselves up with some music. Will you sing to me?"

It was a warm night in May. The glass doors stood open onto the terrace, and the flames of the candles wavered a little in the air from the garden. Seldom enough could they count on an evening to themselves like this. Mary rose and went over to the instrument.

"What shall I sing?"

An amused look had crept into his eyes. He pretended
to think. "Is there not an English song which goes, 'Bid
me despair, and I'll despair, under that cypress tree'?"

"Of course."

She laid her long, white, tapering hands on the keys and
began Herrick's song. Her voice was even more beautiful
than it had been; fuller, rounder and charged with something it had never held before. The words stole toward
him through the candlelit room:

> *" A heart as soft, a heart as kind,*
> *A heart as sound and free*
> *As in the whole world thou can'st find,*
> *That heart I'll give to thee."*

Her voice broke on the last note, for now amazingly, she
had come to feel it was true. The Dutch monster had
gradually turned into William whom she loved. "Oh, if
we could always be together like this!" she cried involuntarily.

"I know, my dear."

She dabbed at her eyes with a scrap of lace. "I did not
know you knew the song. You never asked for it before."

"I have heard you sing it before—once. I determined
that you should never sing it to me again until I felt sure
that you meant the words."

The velvet-dark eyes looked up at him. "When did I
sing it to you?"

"At St. James's. In the ballroom, when the King asked

for a song. I watched you from the gallery. I thought for a moment that Anne had discovered me."

"What on earth were you doing up in the gallery?"

"Stealing a look at my bride. . . . Do you not remember picking up the dwarf, Gibson, when he fell?"

"Poor Mr. Gibson!" But she did not remember. It all seemed so far away now.

When the time came to visit Haarlem, Mary traveled there halfway by water, and halfway by road. She had grown accustomed to the flat landscape with the enormous sky above. She had grown to love the neat, trim villages where, every morning, pails of clean water were dashed against the bricks of the houses to clean them and the brick footways scrubbed clean till they shone rosy pink.

Men working in the fields stopped respectfully and removed their caps. Women dropped curtseys and small children ran behind the great coach, then dropped off as their village began to retire uncomfortably far behind them. Mary knew when they approached Haarlem, because of the bulb fields which stretched on either side of the road. But the tulip season was over now. The withered flowers still hung from their stems, dyeing each field a different faded color. She thought the fields had their own beauty, so.

They were waiting to receive her, all the city dignitaries. They escorted her to the Town Hall, once the old palace of the Counts of Holland. They wanted to show her the work of their greatest citizen, Frans Hals the painter. He had only been dead a short while, and they had not

appreciated him particularly while he lived. The Women
Guardians of Haarlem Almshouse had commissioned him
out of charity; and he had painted them as they were, with
cold, waxy faces and golden chains round their necks.
Mary shivered, looking at those uncharitable faces, and
passed on quickly to the picture of a banquet, with rich
colors and jollity and movement, reminding her of her
uncle's court.

Then, according to their custom, Mary walked through
some of the streets of the town, escorted by the burgomaster, stopping at pleasure to admire whatever might catch
her eye. The city had built itself up richly again, after
more than one terrible disaster. The Spaniards had taken
it and had massacred the garrison which had held out so
bravely. Yet four years later, the Dutch had thrown the
Spaniards out and had rebuilt their half-ruined town.

In the same spirit, when Haarlem went bankrupt over
the gambling craze for new tulips, it had pulled itself together again. The tulip trade was re-established, on a sane,
business footing. Bulb-growers grew prosperous again.
And Mary glanced with admiration at one fine, tall house
after another; houses filled inside, she knew, with handsome furniture, pictures and silver.

When her tall figure turned a corner and entered yet
another street, one could feel vibrations of excitement
travel along it as news that the Princess of Orange was
approaching traveled from house to house. A small girl
darted out, knelt down before a red-brick house with
green shutters, and started to blow away the dust between

the cracks on the pathway. Mary smiled and patted the child's head as she passed. A curious custom this dust-blowing, which she had seen before, and which would have made Uncle King hold his sides with laughter!

Suddenly she noticed a break in the line of houses. A green line of hedge protecting something from the gaze of passers-by. Mary hurried her slow, gracious pace, curiosity urging her to see what it hid.

The burgomaster, who escorted her, saw what had attracted her attention. "Merely a house, your Highness." His voice held a note of apology. "A house which has closed its gates to the world. The house of Martinus Van Tol's daughter."

"Who is he?"

"He is dead. But his hobby was tulips. A great man he was in his day. Yes, a Doctor of Laws, and a member of prominent Societies. But he spent all he made upon tulips, all but this house here, where his daughter lives still."

"He died long ago?"

"When the great crash came, he died of it. At least that is what people say. But his daughter lives on."

They had now reached the green hedge. Mary laid her hand on the gate. "I will go in and see her."

The escorting crowd waited respectfully outside. Mary set foot on the brick path leading up to the door. She looked up at the house and saw it was a handsome one, but neglected. Every window save one was still shuttered, and the shutters were shabby from want of paint. The garden, however, seemed well kept. Bushes, heavy with the scent of syringa made another snowy inner hedge. And between the white blossoms Mary saw something flame. . . .

It was a tulip, last of a bed of them, the others faded and hanging their heads. But this one, sheltered by the shrub it grew near, had lasted longer. It flaunted its amazing colored head, the like of which she had never seen before.

She drew in her breath sharply. Even William, in all his royal gardens, had nothing so fine as that! "What is it called?"

"He grew it from seed and called it after himself. It was the last he propagated, and he hoped to recoup his fortune by it. But he did not live to do so, and now his daughter refuses to sell one bulb."

A small, round face suddenly pressed itself against the dim glass of the one unshuttered window. Mary saw a pale face with large blue eyes and light flaxen hair scraped back from its brow. The burgomaster made a lordly gesture, summoning its owner to come and open the door.

"The young orphan girl who looks after Madame Van Tol," he explained.

The door flew open. The girl on the threshold bobbed a curtsey, then cast an affrighted glance behind her, as an old voice called, "Who is it, Joanna?"

"It is the Princess herself!"

The room was filled with massive furniture. Although the hall looked bleak enough, all that was left in the house seemed crammed into this one room. The high wardrobes and armoires gleamed with polish. An elaborately carved bed stood in one corner. The bed hangings moved as an old, veined hand pulled them apart from inside it. Mary took a step toward the bed, then stopped to pick up a book, evidently dropped on the floor by the little maid. She read its title with astonishment.

It was an English book.

Madame Van Tol said, "I am honored, your Highness. But there is nothing to bring you here."

"You speak English?" Mary balanced the book in her hand. Already the English words were beginning to look queer and foreign to her.

"My father taught me many languages. He was a cultivated man. I try to teach Joanna here. She speaks and reads it quite well."

The girl looked shyly up into Mary's face. It was an appealing look. Mary put out her hand and drew Joanna to her side, pitying her. What an existence, even for an orphan, to live in this silent house, ministering to a bedridden old woman!

The old woman was speaking again. "I have nothing ready to set before your Highness. I do not know why your Highness should have paused here."

Out of politeness, to reassure her, Mary said, "Your father was a great botanist, like my husband, the Prince. Nowhere, even in our Palace of Honselaarsdijk, have I seen anything so fine as that tulip still blooming in your garden."

A look of gratification came over the old, lined face. "I have a bed of them, but the others are over. They are all my father had to bequeath to me—they, and this house."

Mary hesitated, then said gently, "Would you not be

advised to sell the bulbs and buy yourself comfort for your old age? Surely he would have liked you to do that!"

The gratification died, giving place to a bitter expression. "Forty and more years ago when the crash came he tried to do that. But the Fathers of this City pronounced a ban on all buying and selling."

The burgomaster, standing there uncomfortably in his chain of office said hastily, "The ban has long been lifted. You know that, Madam."

"Too late! My father died of a broken heart. Shall I let others profit by what he cherished?"

Mary saw it was no use talking to anyone with so fixed an idea of revenge. How the old woman must rejoice when that carpet of blazing tulips showed through the hedge before envious eyes! She wanted to create a diversion. Handing the book to the silent girl Joanna, she said kindly, "Will you read me a word or two?"

The child took the book, her hand trembling. (But was she a child? The long skirt, the stiff apron, the hair scraped back under a ribbon snood made it difficult to say.) She read a paragraph in a breathless voice. If she stumbled at first it was because she was nervous. Her articulation became clear and steady. After a minute or two, Mary stopped her.

"Thank you, Joanna. Tell me, how old are you?"

"Fourteen, your Highness."

"You speak English well, besides reading it. If I can ever serve you, let me know, for I am an Englishwoman."

"Joanna"—the voice came abruptly, "fetch a trowel and dig up one of my father's bulbs. One only."

"The Van Tol bulb?" Astonishment sounded in the girl's voice.

"Did you not hear her Highness say that the Prince, with all his possessions, lacked one?"

The girl's long skirts rustled across the floor as she left the room. The old woman had given her order in English. She continued in that language while the burgomaster, who could not understand a word of what was said, stood restlessly, fingering his chain.

"I swore that no one should have what had broken my father's heart. But the Prince saved our nation. Yes, he saved Haarlem itself! He deserves this tribute. Even so, I ask something in return."

Mary had already raised the knitted silk purse dangling from her wrist. She had meant to lay some gold pieces on the table in any case, before leaving. But the old woman saw the gesture and said angrily, "Not that! No money can buy my treasure. I want you to promise me something."

"What is it Madam? If I can, I will promise it gladly."

The old woman turned her head toward the window. "She is out there, Joanna? . . . I sent her away so that she should not overhear. She is fond of me, the child. She weeps when I speak of dying. . . ."

Mary took the frail old hand in her own. "I know what you would ask. Did you not hear me offer it already?"

"I am going to die soon. Who will look after Joanna then? What will she do? Go back to the orphanage and scrub floors? I have trained her to walk lightly, to speak softly, to be well-mannered. But indeed she comes of good stock—like the bulbs."

"I will take her in to my own service—then. I promise
you that."

The girl came back into the room with the bulb in her
hand. She was about to place its soiled roots in the princess' hand, when a gesture from the bed stopped her. "Not
so, Joanna! Does one offer a royal gift so nakedly? Bring
me the silver goblet!"

Wondering, Joanna opened a huge carved wardrobe.
Mary could see it was almost empty, save for some pottery
cups and plates, and something which gleamed behind
them. The girl drew out the goblet. It was two-handled
and massive, and bore a coat of arms and the name
MARTINUS VAN TOL engraved on it.

"Put the bulb inside. Then bring it to me than I may offer
it to her Highness myself."

The burgomaster had stopped fiddling with his jewelry.
His eyes protruded as the goblet, with the withered bulb
inside, was ceremoniously handed over.

"This was my father's drinking cup. The rest of his
silver was sold long ago. Take it to the Stadtholder with
my blessing and thanks. The thanks of the whole of Holland."

Mary bent over the bed and kissed the parchment-white
face. Madame Van Tol sank back on her pillows, exhausted. Joanna curtseyed good-by as they left the room.
Halfway to the street, Mary looked back and waved her
free hand toward the girl watching her from the window.

During the long drive back, Mary sat with the goblet on
her knee. The fields in their faded colors swam past, while

she thought of Joanna, her devotion and gentle ways, and how William had said she should have someone about her who spoke Dutch as well as English. And of how William, for all his apparent coldness, would value this double gift above all the others his grateful country had lavished upon him.

When the bulb flowered, it would bring him joy and for her, remembrance. It was an offering which could not be bought.

bought.

Chapter
Eight

As soon as it was high summer, William took his
young wife to spend the hot months at The House in the
Wood. This was a delightful little palace set among green
trees about a mile or so from The Hague. The trees murmured all day long as the air passed through their leaves.
The rustling, whispering sound brought back to Mary her
childhood days, playing under the great oaks of Richmond
Park.

There was not so much pomp and circumstance here.
She was now sixteen, and could behave like a grand lady
when she had to. But here she became a girl again, picking
up her long skirts and chasing or being chased through the

woodland paths, coming home flushed and breathless, with always a little anxiety in her heart as the palace came into view. Would William have been summoned away again to rejoin his troops?

And it was here, toward the end of August, that Joanna arrived. She carried only a small basket which contained all the clothes she possessed, and her face was still stained with the tears she had shed for old Madame Van Tol's death. Mary received her warmly, comforted her, and adopted her as her own personal maid.

When the woods became golden and the leaves started to drop, Mary got news which made her very happy. Anne was coming to visit her this autumn, and with Anne would come their beloved stepmother, the Duchess of York.

The visitors were to stay in The Hague itself, but Mary would send a carriage for them every day, so that they could be here together as much as possible. There were so many things to show Anne! Mr. Pepys, who kept that famous Diary, had visited The House in the Wood years ago and wrote: "I was never taken up more with a sense of pleasure in my life." And he further noted down the things which gave him most pleasure there. "We went into the garden, wherein are gallant nuts better than ever I saw, and a fine Echo under the house in a vault made on purpose with pillars, where I played on my flageolette to great advantage."

The nuts would be ripe by the time Anne came. They would gather them together. And they would test the

Echo, too. Even now, sometimes, when her stiff Dutch
ladies in waiting weren't there, Mary and Joanna would
descend to that vaulted room and throw their voices toward
each other, laughing together at the result.

"But you must leave me Joanna, and wait on my sister,"
Mary told her. "The poor Princess Anne doesn't know a
word of Dutch."

"Leave you Madam?" Joanna looked apprehensive.

"Only for the length of the visit," Mary assured her.
"You and she are the same age, too. She will be thankful
to have someone young about her."

Anne had grown taller, but she was still too plump.
Mary, knowing Anne's love of sweetmeats, put a special
jar of them in her room, because Lady Frances was not
there to forbid them. Anne took in her new surroundings
with large blue eyes, but said little. She never responded
to anything much, although the sight of the bathroom
with its taps and running water moved her to slow admiration.

Mary Beatrice responded more quickly. She hugged her
"dear Lemon" as she had nicknamed Mary, and went
through the rooms of The House in the Wood admiring
the fine furniture and the handsome pictures.

"It is all so clear and bright! Not like dirty old Whitehall! Still"—she corrected herself for fear of sounding criti-
cal of her husband's surroundings—"the cold of the Dutch
winters! I couldn't endure them. How do you keep yourself warm?"

Mary pointed proudly to the great porcelain stoves,

unlit now. "The rooms are as warm as toast, I assure you."

Mary Beatrice was tactful. She pretended great interest in the china cupboards or in anything else which took her fancy, telling the sisters they must go out into the woods without her. So Anne and Mary set out to look for mushrooms, each with a basket and unattended.

As soon as they had stepped into the shadow of the trees Anne said, "Why did you and William not invite Father, too?"

"Of course we did. But he said that Admiralty business kept him at home." Mary stooped to pick a berry and put it in her mouth. When it had gone down she added, "Perhaps it was just as well. He and William would never have got on together."

"You used to love him," Anne said.

Mary remembered the cold face with which her father had told her of her marriage, and was silent. The two girls walked on, with the dry leaves rustling beneath their feet. Then Mary spoke in a grown-up tone. "Marriage divides as well as unites," she said. "Has he spoken of a marriage for you?"

Anne shrugged her shoulders. "It depends upon what the King wants. Father would want a Catholic marriage, but the King has spoken once or twice of a Danish prince."

Mary looked at her sister in astonishment. Could Anne really care so little about the kind of husband chosen for her? Anne caught the meaning in Mary's glance more quickly than usual. "One would get accustomed to anyone

I suppose, so long as he's kind. You seem happy enough with William, and look at the tears you shed!"

"I did not know him then."

"Exactly. But it is another marriage that London is talking of now. Did you know that Sarah—my dear friend Sarah Jennings—got secretly married to Colonel Churchill?"

"Secretly!" Mary frowned. "I don't like that word. It savors of underhandedness."

As usual, Anne sprang in defense of her friend. "How else could they marry?" She asked indignantly. "Sarah has nothing and Colonel Churchill has only his sword. And they've loved each other for years! I'm Sarah's best friend. She told me about it. Someday I mean——"

"Someday?"

"Nothing." Anne spoke rather sullenly. She stooped, pretending to fasten her shoe.

Mary said, "I know what you were going to say. If neither Mary Beatrice nor I have a son, you may be Queen of England some day. Then you could help the Churchills. Isn't that what you meant?"

"Yes," Anne said defiantly. "I don't think I want to be a queen. I hope you will live a long, long time. But if ever I am Queen, I shall make Colonel Churchill a duke!"

Mary began to walk on again as if she had not heard. Anne trotted after her, looking rather ashamed. "You haven't asked for our cousin Monmouth," she panted after a while.

Mary slackened her pace so that the other could reach her side. "How is he?"

"He sent you his love. He's been up in Scotland putting down the Presbyterians. Uncle King says the Scotch are a thorn in his side. Always rebelling."

"They have a right to worship in their own way. It is a pity the King has tried to force them to use the English prayer book."

Anne looked up, shocked, into her sister's face. "Of course they're Cal—Calvinists. And William's a Calvinist too. That's why you talk that way."

Mary felt it was time to turn the conversation. She asked, "Does the King still dote on Monmouth?"

Anne nodded, pursing up her lips. "He would give him anything in the world! Sometimes though, I'm afraid for him."

Mary stopped in the middle of the path. "Afraid—for Monmouth?"

Anne gave another important nod. "The people spoil him so! They're all terrified of what may happen when Father comes to the throne and they have a Catholic king and queen. And Monmouth plays up to that. To being a Protestant I mean."

"You talk nonsense, Anne."

"I don't. They call him the Protestant Duke. He steals all the popularity away from our father. He does it on purpose, I'm sure. Sarah says he does."

A shadow seemed to have crept over the wood, for Mary suddenly felt cold. "Let us go back to the house," she said quickly, taking Anne's hand and almost pulling her round on the path. "Mary Beatrice will be tired of waiting for us. . . ."

That night there was a ball and a supper party for the visitors. The windows of The House in the Wood glowed with candlelight through the dark. The dancing and music put their conversation out of Mary's mind, but she remembered it again, once she was alone with William.

"I'm afraid for our cousin Monmouth." She found herself echoing Anne's words.

She hoped William would contradict her. But instead, he said slowly, "Monmouth is weak. Flattery goes to his head. Someday he may go too far."

"But the King——"

William laid his hand affectionately on her shoulder. "If you are disturbed, dear heart, I can assure you of this. King Charles will never punish him. He is safe as long as his father lives."

She grasped at his words. "Are you sure?"

He stood thoughtfully silent a moment, as though making up his mind about something. Then he spoke with decision. "I will tell you a secret, Mary. The last time I was in England, his Majesty spoke to me about his son. He said that Monmouth might, someday, behave in a foolishly headstrong way. And that the King to satisfy his government, would have to appear to punish him."

"*Appear?*" Mary echoed.

"The King knows his own weakness as well as other people's! He told me the punishment would take the form of banishing Monmouth over to Holland. And that he might even be forced to request me to treat Monmouth as an ordinary political prisoner."

She stared at him in horror. "To put him in prison! You couldn't do that—even to please the King!"

William smiled. "But I need not obey his Majesty, need I? Not if he doesn't want me to!"

She began to understand, partly at least. Charles so often said one thing and meant another. But . . . "How can you tell what he wants?"

"He drew a seal out of his pocket and bade me study it well. If any order comes from him sealed with *that* seal, I am to obey. Otherwise . . ." William paused, shrugging his shoulders.

"Our uncle is a very cunning man," Mary said slowly.

"And he loves his son above everything," William replied.

Chapter
Nine

Each spring the Van Tol tulip blossomed, and multiplied. Mary loved to see the quiet look of pleasure on William's face as he looked at the old woman's gift. But his visits were only snatched ones; Europe was not yet at peace, Holland' might be invaded again at any moment, and he had to be with the troops massed on the frontiers.

Mary was now devotedly in love with her husband. She felt her heart broken, each time that he rode away. But she was very young still. She found ways of passing the time. And she grew more beautiful every day. There were some who considered her the most beautiful woman in Europe.

She had hobbies which helped to pass the empty hours when William was not there. She was an exquisite embroidress, and she also painted delicate miniatures. Such fine work which could be held up to the eyes, suited her shortsightedness. She was also a good musician. Years ago, when she was a little girl, Samuel Pepys had praised her for her good ear and execution. And he knew about music himself, as well as about keeping diaries.

Music was the fashion in Holland anyway. Every night in summer the leaded windows of the great merchants' houses stood open along the canals. One could catch glimpses of families gathered about the harpsichord, and hear snatches of thin, sweet music, or singing. Even the songs of Purcell and Byrd found their way from England across the channel, to be sung along with the folk songs of Holland itself.

One heard other music, too, in the streets. Soldiers on leave, swaggering along by the bridges, shouted out songs of the camp. Mary sometimes caught a bar or two of them when in Amsterdam or The Hague, and smiled, thinking that William must know them well. The catch song of the time was "Lillibuleero," a stupid jingle with its refrain Lilli-lilli-lillibuleero! She sometimes hummed it herself.

When William returned, she eagerly shared the interests which took his mind off the dangerous situation in Europe. But sometimes she wondered, too, that a man so reserved and cold, so wrapped up in military problems, should care so intensely for beauty! The fragile beauty of flowers entranced him. Together they catalogued their favorites with enchanting names like The Cherry of Arabia, The Silver Lotus, The Crystal Rose . . .

Perhaps they reminded him of Mary herself. For the secret core of his own heart was not cold. She had awakened it to warmth and fire.

The only thing that grieved them was that they had no children. Nor had Mary Beatrice managed to give her husband a living son. The Duke of York wrote often to Mary, and at first she was touched to receive his letters. Then, puzzled, she began to discern a note in them she did not like. They paid compliments to William but sneered at him, too. Was it possible that her father was trying to sow trouble between William and her?

No actual record survives to prove this. Yet something certainly happened. Dutch memoirs of the time hint at some such deliberate attempt; an attempt discovered and repudiated by Mary. Her early love for her father had received one blow already, when he showed himself so indifferent to her tears at her marriage. It is pretty certain that her remaining affection for him received its death blow about this time.

She began to fill her mind with other things, so as to forget this sorrow. She became interested, then fascinated, by the Oriental porcelain brought into Holland by the ships of the East India Company. She started to make her valuable collection and became very knowledgable about china. She even helped Joanna to wash and polish the delicate pieces when they were first unpacked from their crates. It was a pleasure to her to wear a small apron like any ordinary Dutch housewife, and to feel the translucent ware, cool between her finger tips.

One day Joanna came to her bashfully, to say she was engaged to be married.

Mary received a shock. "But you're too young!" she exclaimed.

Joanna said boldly, "Pardon, your Highness. I'm a full year older than you were yourself, when you married."

It was true. The child was sixteen now. Two years had already passed since that visit to Haarlem. "Who is it?" Mary asked.

"Highness, his name is Jan Paltz. Captain Jan Paltz. He is one of the palace guards."

There were so many about the palace, and Mary did not remember the name. She could understand how the pretty girl would attract his attention. But she wanted to satisfy herself that he was worthy of Joanna.

"Where is he? I want to speak to him."

"He's off duty, Madam. But he—he said he would wait in the Park to hear if your Highness approved."

"Go and fetch him." A better idea struck her. Here, in the palace, he would be formal and not show his true character. Better far to catch him out of doors and unawares!

"No. We shall go and find him. I want a breath of fresh air anyway."

They were at Honselaarsdijk, where Mary had lingered this year into the summer. They passed along the great terrace and down the stone steps, threading their way through the flower beds, toward the entrance into the Park. Shady walks led past white marble statuary toward a small stream with a rustic bridge. Mary saw her companion's eyes light up at the sight of the figure leaning over the bridge with his back turned toward them.

So the child is really in love! she thought, and wondered what sort of a man this was. He was singing to himself to pass the time. She heard the refrain she was beginning to tire of, coming to them from over the water: "Lilli-lilli-lillibuleero—"

He turned when he heard their footsteps, and at the sight of Mary, saluted and bowed. She saw with relief that he looked a simple young fellow, a real soldier, not as she feared, a courtier-soldier who would only be amusing himself with someone so simple and unimportant as Joanna.

She gave her enchanting smile and said, "So I hear you wish to take away my favorite?"

He said stoutly, "I wish to marry Joanna, your Highness. I promise to make her as good a husband as I can."

She looked at his uniform and said, "You have served under the Prince?"

"Many times." He spoke with pride. "I'm only a plain soldier and to speak freely, I would rather do my duty on the battlefield than waste it here——"

"Jan!" The girl looked shocked, but Mary only smiled, saying, "Some of you must take your turn here. I think I prefer a man who does not covet the life among courts."

"I'm a plain farmer's son and I don't know the way of courts, only to do my duty."

Mary asked, "And when your term of service is over?"

"Why then I'll go back to the land where I belong. Joanna won't want for solid comfort though 'tis but a small farm that I'll inherit. And if I married her soon, before she's got time to be spoiled by luxury——"

Again an affrighted look from Joanna, but Mary laughed aloud. "She's a good girl, and I haven't spoiled her, I promise you! She will make an excellent farmer's wife. I shall give her a dowry too, so you can buy more land."

The young fellow flushed. "Thank ye, Madam, but I had no thought of that when I asked her to marry me. I'm willing to take her as she is."

So Joanna was married. Her mistress attended the wedding and gave her her wedding clothes as well as the dowry she had promised. Joanna could not feel any more devotion and gratitude than she felt already. But Mary was sad at parting with the gentle girl who had spoken English with her and who seemed more like a daughter, somehow, in spite of there being only two years' difference between them.

Time passed. The next wedding was Anne's. It took place in 1683 and the bridegroom was Prince George of Denmark. Again this wedding was by the King's desire, to pacify the people. The Prince was a Protestant, but otherwise Mary could find little attractive about him. True, William said he was a good soldier and a brave man, but he was also stupid and dull. Anne did not seem to mind. There were no tears about this wedding. And afterward, she wrote to her sister happily enough.

Perhaps Anne did not know the verdict pronounced on her new husband by King Charles, who found him even more boring than he had found William. "I've tried him drunk and I've tried him sober," the King had said, amid roars of laughter, "and there's nothing in him."

Mary could not go to her own sister's wedding. She had to preside over William's court when he was so often absent with his army. She could only write long, affectionate letters to Anne, and send her presents of tea. It was a strange, new drink and Anne (always fond of food and drink) seemed to adore it. She kept writing to Mary for more. The Dutch East India merchants had just introduced tea to Holland. They said the Chinese drank it all day. Some people made the mistake, at first, of boiling the leaves like a vegetable and then eating them with butter. Soon, however, they learned how to infuse tea properly. It became the fashionable craze, mostly because it was so expensive.

Mary sent the tea over to Anne in beautiful lacquered boxes, green or red.

About this time, too, some trading ships began to bring strange cargo across the North Sea. The ships had come from Scottish ports, and their cargo was human. Severe men, leading frightened wives and children, stepped off their decks onto what was to them foreign soil. The strangers knew no Dutch, though they took care to learn it soon enough. They had to, if they were to earn their living here. If they were not particularly welcomed, at least they were not hindered. For the authorities turned a strangely blind eye on them, neither asking whence they came nor what they were doing here in Holland.

Mary first became aware of them during a visit to Utrecht. It was winter now, and the snow fell in the quiet streets, powdering the tall cathedral spire. Around the walls of the city, following the curve of the old moat, lay the frozen waters of a canal. This was called the Oude Gracht, and was a favorite place for skating in winter. It shone darkly like steel save where the winter sun caught the scores on its surface. Old men employed by the town stood by leaning on their brooms, ready to sweep off the newly fallen snow. And all day, so long as any light remained in the sky, the clash and ring of skates was heard, as figures circled like toys on the ice.

Mary had not yet learned to skate. She and one of the ladies in waiting were pushed across the ice in a gilded sledge shaped like a swan, while, a little way off, William skated by himself, hands behind his back, eyes darting over his subjects, who were enjoying themselves at a respectful distance. It struck Mary that he appeared to be looking for someone. But she forgot this as something else chained her attention.

"Look! Those gentlemen over there—they do not seem Dutch. They look more—more like people from my own country!"

The stout Dutch lady in waiting glanced over her shoulder. Two men and a boy were skating clumsily by themselves, over in the shadow of the walls. Their very inexpertness showed they were foreign, still learning the national winter pastime. But their clothes showed it, too. Dark gray instead of rich black, thick wool instead of velvet or face-cloth, bone buttons not silver. . . .

Yet they carried themselves like gentlemen, too.

The lady in waiting giggled. "I was told they were English. Your Highness knows I speak English pretty well. And yet when I caught a snatch of them talking, I couldn't understand a word!"

The sledge made a half-loop toward them over the ice. The three strangers, taken unawares, made one or two steps backwards before royalty, and the elder of the two men called out to the boy, "Come awa' laddie! Dinna conter the Princess."

"That's Scots speech, not English." Mary knew the accent well. She had heard it spoken by the Scots nobles at her uncle's court. It gave her a sudden stab of homesickness. "I must speak to them . . ."

Suddenly she heard William's voice in her ear. He had swooped silently over to the sledge and was now directing it away from the strangers. "No, my dear. Leave them alone. It is best not to be seen speaking to such persons."

"But why?" She was puzzled. It seemed to her as though they might be the very persons William was searching for. Certainly she had the impression that he had paused and spoken to them before skating over to take her away.

"I shall tell you presently." He gave a warning glance toward the listening figure of the lady in waiting.

Now the sky which had cleared, grew heavy again with

snow. It was getting dark, too, and some of the town lights were already lit. Mary's sledge took her over to the bank where their carriage was waiting. They got into it and were driven off to one of the merchant's houses, which had been put at their disposal during their visit to Utrecht.

It stood flush with the cobbled street, looking onto the waters of a canal. Inside, the richness of its furnishings belied the severe simplicity of its frontage. Blocks of solid black and white marble floored the hall while the richly carved furniture shone with polishing until it reflected the candlelight from the brass chandeliers above.

Its owner received them in the hall. He performed this courtesy each time they re-entered it. His fortune was founded upon Utrecht velvet, which in those days rivaled even that of Venice. He wore a suit of his own factory's weaving of mulberry red, rich and sober, with a gold chain about his neck. He bowed low, then retired, for unless William invited him, he was too proud to force himself upon them at supper.

And William gave him no invitation. He preferred to sup alone with his wife, though Mary for her part would have hesitated to be ungracious to a man in his own house. She gave William a pleading look. He paid no attention but strode forward to the little supper room reserved for them both.

Another canal ran by the back of the house, but more closely without any intervening street to prevent its frozen waters grinding against the brickwork of the building itself. Only that morning, Mary had stepped into a bigger

sledge drawn up to steps leading straight down from the
back door onto the ice. She thought of that sledge drive
with pleasure; how the little vehicle had taken her all
through the hidden waterways of the city.

She lifted her spoon to begin her soup, then laid it
down suddenly.

"Listen! A sledge is pulling up by the back door instead
of the front. Can't you hear it?"

William rose, pushed back one of the high carved shutters, and peered out into the night. The room they were
in, looked onto this secret canal. And Mary's quick ears
had certainly heard the sliding jar of a sledge pulled up
sharp, the muttered, indistinguishable sound of men's
voices below.

"I know who it is," he said calmly, replacing the shutter
and sitting down again to his soup.

Both preferred, when they could, to have no one waiting upon them all the time. They had little enough privacy as it was. But even though they were alone, Mary
refrained from asking the obvious question. She had
learned to do so when she saw that look on her husband's
face.

She waited until he had finished his soup. Then she
picked up the silver handbell to summon a footman. At
the same moment, the folding doors behind William were
suddenly thrown open. His favorite friend and lifelong
attendant, Mijnheer Keppel, slipped through, closing the
doors again quickly behind him.

But Mary had had a glimpse of the two men standing in

the room beyond. Keppel said something to William in Dutch. William flung down his napkin and followed the other into the anteroom beyond.

She sat there waiting. There was only that faint murmur of voices from the other side of the door. The intonation sounded English, though she could not be sure. She rose, and pushing back the shutter once more, looked out into the night. It was bitterly cold outside. The air cut like a knife. The backs of the other houses bordering the canal had their windows all shuttered securely against it, so that no light showed, except the one light immediately under her, the light from the lantern tied to the sledge drawn up on the ice below.

She shivered, closed the shutter and stepped back into the room. She sat down at the table again and waited. Presently the murmuring stopped. The folding doors opened again and William stepped through them. He went to a side table and began to carve from some of the meats waiting kept hot over dishes of live charcoal. Mary asked her question at last.

"Were those not the two Scotch gentlemen who were on the Oude Gracht?"

He did not seem displeased after all, but nodded and said, "Keppel generally searches out the latest arrivals from Britain so as to obtain news of what is happening there. I don't always tell you because it might distress you to hear how your father adds to his unpopularity day by day."

She understood now. How thoughtful and how just

William was! Recently in Scotland there had been rebellion and fighting. Even great Scottish nobles had lost their
estates and been forced to fly abroad for their lives if they
had taken any part in the insurrections. Most of them had
come here, to Holland. This gave William a difficult role
to play. On the one hand, he wished to protect the refu-
gees, here because the form of religion they practiced was
the same as his own. On the other hand both he and his
wife were closely related to the man who had sent them
into exile. Their greatest enemies were Mary's own father
and uncle. . . .

She was looking at him across the candle flames. Another question trembled on her lips, but she was afraid to
ask it. Instead, she said, "Why do they choose to come to
Utrecht?"

He smiled. "Because of the education here. The Scotch
have a craving for it, as you know. And Utrecht University
is world famous."

"I would not have thought them able to pay the fees,
poor creatures."

"Oh, they work. They work well, at anything they can
get. I give them a helping hand occasionally."

It was like William to do this quietly, without telling
her until now. She said, "I am sure they are grateful to
you. Even if—circumstances allow them to go back to Scotland, they will always remember you, William."

He gave her a shrewd glance and said, "I hope so. I
should, in any case, have aided them so far as was possible
without offending our uncle too much. But it may happen

in future that their gratitude stands us in good stead."

She saw quickly what he was hinting at. Should her father have no other heir but herself, there might come a time when the gratitude of the Scotch nobles would be useful in support of her claim. But she disliked the thought of that future. She wished for nothing, not even a crown, unless it was shared with William. She was glad when he began to speak again, about something else.

"Keppel has also gleaned some news from our uncle's American colonies. Sir William Penn actually plans to build a city to be called Philadelphia! One of his Quaker notions I suppose. The name means the City of Brotherly Love."

But her thoughts still disturbed her, so that she only said sadly, "There's little enough of that abroad."

His quick mind had darted on to something else. "Penn cannot have civilization unless he introduces colleges and schools. We must see to that, Mary, if it ever lies in our power."

To push the possibilities at which he kept hinting out of her mind, she asked her question at last.

"Did the Scotch gentlemen bring any news of Monmouth?"

William instantly looked grave. "He risks danger with his pretensions. I hear his triumphal progresses through the country are made as though he were king already."

"What does he do?" she asked pleadingly. "He can surely move about as he pleases!" Then, as her husband remained silent: "He has always been called the Protestant Duke—even hailed as such. That isn't the same as calling oneself King!"

"Perhaps not. But he acts as though he were. Even to touching for the King's Evil."

"No!" She drew her breath in sharply.

The common people were convinced that a touch from the Sovereign's own hand could cure the skin disease they called the King's Evil. She remembered, long ago, seeing her uncle extend his hand to some poor creature begging for the miracle to be vouchsafed. She had once asked him, "Do you believe it really can cure?" Now, sharply and suddenly there came to her from the past, King Charles's lazy smile, and his very words.

"What does it matter, my lass? It is they who do the believing. I am only the Lord's Anointed!"

The Lord's Anointed. Monmouth was acting that part now; not just the part of the Protestant Duke. She could imagine the grace with which he put out his hand to give the King's Touch. . . .

William had risen from table. The meal was over. He was saying, "I think we shall have more snow tomorrow.

She did not reply. She sat there, listening to the faint sounds which reached the room through the thickness of the shuttered window. The groans and scrapings of the sledge as it started its journey once more, taking the two Scotsmen away, over the ice.

 Chapter
Ten

That winter, the winter of 1683—1684, London had
its hardest spell of frost within living memory. The Thames
actually froze so that Mary Beatrice (who wrote descriptions
of it to her "Dear Lemon") said she was having the greatest
fun in the world, being driven in a sledge hung with bells,
all the way on the ice from the Temple to Westminster.

Mary dropped the letter into her lap. Although the
view from her window looked over the pure, clear Dutch
landscape, she was not looking at it. Her mind's eye saw
the great river Thames, on whose banks she had passed all
her youth. She knew how that fog which always comes, in
London, with frost, would shed a golden haze down on it.

And through the haze, laughing and muffled in furs, would glide her pretty stepmother heralded by the sledge bells. . . .

Anne wrote about the phenomenon too. But her interests were more material. She told of the ox roasted whole on the ice and how delicious it had smelt. Of the enterprising printer who had set up a booth where he issued slips, at sixpence each, containing your name, the date, and the words "River Thames" printed on them as souvenirs. Of horse racing and bull baiting, even, all on the ice.

The whiff of a London fog was still in Mary's nostrils as she stared out of one of the windows in The House in the Wood. William had come here to hunt. You could see the small prints of the deer under the trees where the snow piled up as it fell from the branches above. The Wood was so near The Hague, the sport was tamer than that found in the great forests of Guelderland. But William, too, was receiving intelligence from England. And here he could receive it more easily.

Mary smiled to herself as she remembered her tears at marrying William. It seemed long ago now. She had been but a foolish child. For she had known a long while now that William was the only man in the world she could love.

The Wood outside was growing misty. Soon William would ride back, hungry for supper. She must dress to please him, dress in the new French fashion which suited her excellently. She rang her hand bell and immediately one of her ladies parted the curtains which divided the room and came forward. She was a plump, elderly Dutch-woman of noble family, who dressed in the unbecoming way of the Court; always in black, velvet in winter, satin in summer; the neck filled in with white tuckers and the hair frizzed over a high, polished forehead.

"I must dress now, Baroness. Please summon my maids."

The candles were lit in the tall silver candlesticks on her dressing table. Between them lay a piece of paper containing a fashion print. It had been engraved in Paris, and it showed the French ladies of the Court of King Louis, walking about Versailles in all their splendor. The Protestant world might be at war with France, but France still ruled the fashions. Mary had had several dresses made in the new style already. Her maids slipped one on. It was cut low enough to scandalize the elderly lady in waiting who stood by, muffled up to the neck. But Mary's own neck was as white as a swan, and it rose triumphant over her bared shoulders.

"Now my hair . . ." Somebody tied a peignoir over those shoulders, and the creamy lace foamed over her dress, protecting it. She gave her instructions, slowly in Dutch, to the hairdresser. Now and then she leaned forward to examine, shortsightedly, the style of hairdressing in the picture. The masses of blue-black hair were combed back from the beautiful forehead instead of being teased over it into the tangled fringe of the fashion of twenty years ago, still current at the Dutch Court. The lady in waiting looked on in horror. . . .

"Now—the curl."

The hairdresser brushed one lock of hair expertly round his finger, then let it lie, one long glossy curl, down Mary's left shoulder. The effect was ravishing. Better still, it was new.

William came in that evening, tired from his hunting. He did not appear to notice any change in his wife's appearance. Instantly she sensed that his mind, temporarily relaxed by his favorite sport, had gone back to some problem of its own. She could guess what that problem was.

"You have had more news from England?"

She waited anxiously for his answer. During last summer, a conspiracy called the Rye House Plot had been discovered. It aimed at curbing the power of King Charles. But a subsidiary plot had also been discovered. This actually had as its goal the assassination of both Charles and his brother. Fortunately the plotters were discovered in time. Some were still in hiding, but almost daily they were being caught and hanged or executed for high treason.

One of the names connected with the first Plot was that of James Monmouth, the Protestant Duke. But his enemies over in England claimed that he was also implicated in the second.

William did not answer immediately. Mary burst out, "He would have nothing to with his father's death! You know that!"

They understood each other now, as one person. William did not need to ask who she meant. He nodded gravely. "Monmouth claims he was not even told of the further plot. The King himself believes he is innocent of any desire to murder. But he must punish him for his participation in the other matter."

"Of—of course."

"Four of Monmouth's best friends have already been executed. He is lucky to get off with banishment."

Mary was silent. She had known, weeks ago, that her cousin had had to leave England. He was in Brussels, so she was told. Why did he not come here to them?

Once more William guessed her thoughts. "He is not sure how I would receive him. He is discredited with the King, and in addition he is your father's chief enemy. It would ill become him to thrust himself on us until he is sure of a welcome."

Mary colored. "He would always get a welcome from me."

"I dare say, my dear. But I am the ruler of Holland, and I must not compromise my country."

"Oh, of course." She hung her head a little, and William, to lighten the taste of his rebuke, said teasingly, "What does that long curl do on your shoulder? Is it a new fashion?"

Reviving she teased him back. "All the world copies the fashions of Versailles whether the ruler of Holland fights France or not!"

Presently the snow melted, and the winter was past. The armies of Europe came out of their winter quarters and William rode off to join his men. He had long since freed the rich, important cities of The Netherlands, but the French were continually nibbling at his frontiers, retaking this province or that, and causing him to exercise eternal vigilance. Mary waved him good-by with an aching heart as, now, she always did.

She found the days unendurably long without William.

The parterres under the palace windows at Honselaarsdijk soon blazed with color again. The Court had moved, as usual, to this palace as soon as spring came. Its golden balconies once more gleamed in sunshine, freed of their burden of snow.

Once more the great porcelain stoves were allowed to die out so that the sweet spring air could enter the rooms. There came a spell of warm weather, early for the time of year. Mary, walking along the terrace and pausing beside the vivid carpet of Van Tol tulips, was reminded of Joanna and struck by an idea.

She would make one of her barge journeys through the fields. She would pay a visit to Joanna's home so as to see Joanna's new baby! She had already sent the baby a handsome christening present. Jan Paltz had finished his service, and the farm he worked could be reached (as most places could) by water. It was in the same province as Honselaarsdijk. The expedition would give Mary something to do and take her mind off the possible effects of damp fields on William's chest.

It was a delightful scheme! The royal barge was painted crimson and gold, so that it gleamed like some exotic bird winging slowly over the water. It had a silk canopy to keep the sun off her as she sat, with a lady in waiting to read aloud if the slow passage through the flat landscape grew monotonous. A white horse plodded along the towpath, drawing the barge by a rope. The reeds rustled in the wake of the barge, and wild fowl darted out now and then, paddling out of the way for dear life on little webbed feet.

Mary had her embroidery on her lap, but she left it there. The bulb fields made real, living patterns of color on each side of her. The industry was well established now all over Holland. The tragedy engulfing Martinus Van Tol and thousands of others, had long been forgotten. Presently, when the flowers faded, the bulbs would be stacked and dried out and sent to many places outside Holland itself. Mary had sent Anne some already. She wondered how they were doing in London's sooty soil. . . .

The small villages swam slowly past. Each had its church spire growing up like a stem toward the clouds. The fat white clouds themselves seemed to touch the horizon. Now and then the barge would swim majestically right through the heart of some little village or township, as the canal cut through it. Then everyone would come out of their houses to stand on the bank and stare. And the children would cheer, and old men raise their hats toward the lovely lady sitting there under her silken canopy. In a moment or two, the gleam of red and gold would be gone, the plodding hoofs of the tracehorse would die in the distance. And men returning from work elsewhere in the evening would be greeted by their wives saying, "The Princess passed through our town today."

At last, the man leading the white horse pointed and called, "Highness, there lies the farm of Jan Paltz."

The patchwork fields around it were sown with grain, not bulbs. In the middle of them stood a comfortable-looking brick house with a deep thatched roof and a small yard. The day was so quiet and still, Mary could hear the hens clucking in the yard even from this distance away.

"I shall descend here."

The man guiding the barge with a long pole, gave it a shove and sent it into the bank. He jumped ashore and gave his hand to the Princess. A tiny path running alongside the field wound upward toward the farm. As Mary and her lady in waiting approached it, a dog barked furiously, and a man came from round the back of the house to see what was the matter.

It was Jan Paltz, though Mary hardly recognized him at first. Gone was the swagger figure in uniform. He had grown into a burly, square countryman, and though he had no plumed hat to sweep off at her approach, he dropped on one knee when he saw who it was.

"I have come to see my god son. You called him William, after the Prince?"

"Of course, your Highness. He's a fine baby though I say so. And Joanna will be out of her mind with happiness when she sees you. She's getting the dinner ready."

He talked as he escorted her into the yard, pointing out his new barn proudly, and all the improvements he had made. Mary smiled as if she were listening, but his words suddenly meant nothing, for she had heard the wail of a baby who feels himself neglected. . . .

She hurried into the yard and stooping over the carved wooden cradle by the kitchen door, scooped up the child and hugged it.

The little boy stopped crying at once. Joanna came running out, stopped in amazement, then, as neither of Mary's hands were free to be kissed, took a corner of her silk sleeve and pressed it to her lips.

"Your Highness! You do us such honor. . . . Believe me, the baby was crying only for attention. He is well fed; in fact he is spoiled——"

"He is a beautiful child." Mary laid the plump, strong baby back on his pillows. A sharp feeling of sorrow shot through her. For all their position and state, neither Anne nor she had what this simple couple had been given by Providence. Several times she and William had been disappointed in their hopes of a child. Her stepmother, Mary Beatrice, had had one or two weakly children, but they had not survived.

Joanna, seeing the shade on her former mistress's face and guessing its meaning, laid her hand again on Mary's sleeve, but this time to pull her gently into the house. "We were just going to have our meal. It is very simple. But if your Highness would deign——"

Always ready to be kind, Mary instantly forgot her pang of envy. She sat down in the spotless kitchen with its floor of red brick, and its blue and white pottery plates set out already upon the scrubbed wooden table. Joanna could scarcely eat for stealing glances at her adored lady. Jan, whose appetite was keen after a morning's work in the fields, only paused to offer the Princess every dish first before falling upon it himself and eating very heartily indeed. The lady in waiting toyed with the coarse food, thinking longingly of the cold chicken and fruit on the barge, and was greatly relieved when the visit came to an end.

As they rose, Mary made a sign to the Baroness, who produced a silver cup from the velvet bag she was carrying. "It has your son's name on it," Mary said as she handed it to Joanna, pointing to WILLIAM engraved on one side.

"But your Highness already sent him a handsome christening present. Twenty pieces of gold!"

"Never mind. This is to remind you of the silver goblet you presented to me for the Prince. Do you remember?"

Joanna's eyes sparkled. "Dr. Van Tol's own goblet! Does—does the Prince sometimes drink from it?"

Mary nodded and said good-by. They accompanied her to the edge of the canal, Joanna carrying the baby against her shoulder. And the child woke up and bellowed again at the noise the trace horse made starting along the towpath once more.

Slowly the sun inclined toward the west, and the fields turned from green to gold in its slanting rays. The air had grown chill by the time the barge approached the palace again. There it lay, enclosed in its ornamental gardens skirted by the canal. As they drew nearer, the clipped hedges seemed to shoot up, engulfing the Palace once more.

Mary shivered a little as she hastened from the barge through the ornamental gardens, up the stone steps and across the terrace into the hall. This hall was a vast domed place of marble, through which every footstep or voice was echoed and magnified. Out from it ran the long galleries lined with William's collection of pictures. The galleries turned sharply to right and left out of the hall. The hall itself was empty but it echoed with sound. The sound of a man's voice talking in English, somewhere out of sight.

He must be in the left-hand gallery. Astonished, she ran down the hall and stopped at the end. Now she could see down the whole length of it, hung with magnificent specimens of the Dutch School of Painting on one side, lit by the windows opposite.

The voice was saying loudly, "For my part, I prefer your interiors by Vermeer. There, and in paintings of still life, you Dutch are pre-eminent, while our School of Portraiture . . ."

She recognized the voice with its North-country accent. And the nearest mirror reflected that dwarflike figure, standing, legs apart, before the Vermeer, lecturing an amused Dutch courtier upon the differences between the Dutch and English schools of painting.

It was her old painting master, Richard Gibson. But even while she hurried with joy to meet him, she wondered what sort of news had brought him so unexpectedly: Was it a good or bad omen that he had come?

 Chapter
Eleven

The little man turned around sharply at the sound of her approach.

"My lady! I'm rejoiced to see ye again. And looking more beautiful than ever!"

He kissed both her hands, then stepped back for another look. "Plumper, but it sets ye fine enough. Not heavy like the Princess Anne——"

Mary caught the shocked look of the courtier and had to choke back a laugh. "Mr. Gibson is a privileged person," she explained, adding, "He taught me many valuable lessons when I was a girl. He can say what he likes."

But now that the dwarf had shown his pleasure at seeing

her, his mind reverted to the picture before him. "I was pointing out to this gentleman how light diffused, as Monsieur Vermeer has it, gives a realistic effect which escapes Monsieur Rembrandt for all chiaroscuro lacks. Yet it would ill become me——"

"To criticize a fellow artist?" Mary smiled, looking down on him affectionately from her tall height. Then her expression changed. "What has brought you over to Holland so unexpectedly?"

The dwarf gave her a sudden, warning glance. Her lady in waiting, her page, the courtier who had first received and tried to entertain him before her return to the palace—nearly all of them could understand and speak English. The gallery was no place for a private conversation.

"Come with me," she said quickly, "I have a picture hanging in my own apartments which I think you will remember."

He followed her until they reached the suite of rooms on the ground floor overlooking the flower beds beneath. The candles were lit already in her sitting room. She picked up a silver candlestick and passed it over the wall with the picture on it, where the evening shadows lay thickest.

"This is the most prized by me."

It was Gibson's wedding present to her. The stiff, labored representation of Richmond looked crude after the Dutch paintings hanging outside in the gallery. But many a time Mary had stood before it, when bouts of homesickness obscured the unexpected pleasures she had found in her new home.

She set the candlestick down again and asked quietly, "What have you come to tell me?"

He tore his eyes unwillingly away from his own handiwork. "Does my lady remember how the Duke of Monmouth always promised to visit her and bring me too?"

She nodded, then understood. "The Duke is here?"

"He left Brussels three days ago. He has already searched out the Prince and asked for his hospitality here, in Holland. His Highness bade me come to you with the message that the Duke will be a welcome guest so far as he is concerned."

"So far as——" It was a strange message for William to send. Surely he ruled the Netherlands and not she!

The dwarf, watching her face, said quickly, "It depends upon whether you wish to incur your father's anger. Angry enough he'd be if he knew you received his chief enemy."

"And William—the Prince—has left me to decide?"

"His Highness has said it would ill become him to make difficulties between parent and child."

There was a long silence in the candlelit room. Outside, the flowery parterres had faded to gray, and a crescent moon now showed through the window glass, its light growing stronger every minute. Richard Gibson waited, stiff with anxiety.

At last Mary said, "Tell the Duke that my husband's wishes are mine."

That night at supper, Mr. Richard Gibson was the life

and soul of the party. When William was absent, Mary supped with her suite, and the courtiers could scarcely hide their amusement at the jokes of the little man who used such a strange English accent. Gibson was a Cumberland man and in his youth had been page to a lady living at Mortlake, where the famous tapestries were woven. She was struck by his talent in drawing, and sent him to work in the tapestry sheds, copying the designs and getting some instruction.

Always full of himself and his own importance, he lectured the Dutch ladies and gentlemen present at supper, on the principles of design which, he said, he had learned through copying the portraits of Sir Peter Lely as much as through anything else. That Holland had her own magnificent school of painting, did not appear to strike him. Sir Peter Lely's nymphs and shepherdesses were to him the highest representations of art. Nor was he in the least bashful among the Dutch aristocrats, any more than he had been among the English ones. Had he not had the honor of being Instructor of Drawing to the Princesses Mary and Anne?

Mary was glad to see that the rather stolid courtiers did not take umbrage at Mr. Gibson's outspoken criticisms of their best artists. They listened indulgently, for they recognized him as the court plaything left over from another age. His finery entertained them, too. He had chosen to appear in his costume as an archer. The green velvet, the silver buttons, the one silver arrow held negligently in his hand as a jewel of office; that only marked him out, in their opinion, as wearing the tinsel of a buffoon.

But Mary knew there was more to him than that. There was a keen brain, and fierce loyalty, and perhaps the same mind of a plotter as was in his master, the Duke.

Had William counted the cost of receiving their cousin Monmouth? she wondered. He must have done so, for he never did anything without counting the cost. As for displeasing her father, the time for considering that was gone. The Duke of York had already killed his elder daughter's loyalty by his attacks on her husband. Did not even the scriptures tell a wife to forsake everyone and cleave to her husband?

But her heart was heavy, all the same. And that night she dreamed of her father as the kindly man he had once been toward his children, and not as the selfish bigot he had become.

Richard Gibson left the palace next morning. He neither vouchsafed, nor did Mary inquire, where his master was. Mary told him the Court would be removing to The House in the Wood as it always did about this time. That other little palace was nearer to The Hague and its social functions. Mary preferred it, too, to the cold, isolated magnificence of Honselaarsdijk, where the tulips already were hanging their withered heads, their season of brief glory past for another year.

But The House in the Wood was just stepping into its summer finery. The trees surrounding it were bursting into green and filled with bird song. Mary, lying in her high, four-posted bed in the early morning, could hear the wood pigeons cooing as they lurched across the window sills. Here, in this exquisite house, surrounded by trees and birds, she felt herself awaiting the coming of the fair prince. Would Monmouth come here, or would he wait to enter The Hague with William?

She could not tell which she wanted. She hoped for, yet dreaded, his coming. She knew, if he came, she could not conceal her pleasure and would do him all the honors possible. But then word of her cordial reception would certainly be sent overseas to her father and would hurt him—would seem disloyal. . . .

The air grew more balmy—more like summer. She could walk out now without any cape or wrap. Sometimes she even dispensed with attendants, though that shocked the ladies of the Court. But Mary did not mind. She kilted her skirts up, kicked off her high-heeled slippers and put on leather shoes, and strolled through the woods by herself, following the paths she and Anne had taken five years ago, though it was too early for mushrooms yet.

It was quite safe. The royal foresters, in their uniforms of green with orange, paced the outskirts of the woods, making sure of Mary's safety and privacy. So, when her shortsighted eyes saw a man standing at the end of one of the paths, with his back to a tree, she thought him one of the foresters. She was surprised that, catching sight of her, he did not immediately retire out of sight.

Instead, he advanced. The shadows cast by the trees hid

his face until he had almost reached her. Then she saw it was James Monmouth.

She gave a cry of joy. He grasped her hands and kissed her lightly on each cheek. "So you don't disdain a disgraced man? Thank you, *ma cousine!*"

So Gibson the dwarf had given him her message. Whatever her father might say or think, she could not go back on it now. She was happy that it was so. For here was her playmate, come back to be with her. And, best of all, William approved!

They began to walk slowly out of the wood. Mary said something about having a suite of rooms prepared for him, but Monmouth shook his head.

"You are kindness itself to think of it. But the Prince has already granted me the use of a house in the Lange Voorhout, in The Hague."

"Oh!" She remembered the house. "It belonged to his grandmother. He always said he would keep it for the use of any of his family."

"Exactly. I fear that, judging from my father's state of mind (not to mention *your* father's), I shall be occupying it long enough." He gave her a sideways smile.

She asked apprehensively, "Is the King very angry with you, James?"

Monmouth shrugged his shoulders. "He has to pretend to be. He knows well enough that I would never have countenanced any injury to his person. But that's what my enemies say. They claim I was in that part of the plot as well."

"My father . . ." She faltered, then was silent.

"It suits the Duke of York to discredit me. And it suits the King to appear to punish me; he must do so of course, to satisfy his ministers and give the lie to any gossip about favoritism. After all, when so many have lost their heads over this plot, it would not look well if I didn't lose *something!*"

He laughed as he spoke, and she tried to laugh, too. But the old shadow had fallen on her again, as they approached the lawns and hedges surrounding The House in the Wood. The shadow vanished, however, at the sight of a cavalcade with William in its center, riding up to the porte-cochere. Thank God he was back! He would know how to handle this whole situation so full of danger as well of joy.

William kissed her affectionately, then extended his hand to the handsome cousin who towered above him. It was obvious, from the greeting between the two men, that they had already come to an understanding; and that William was prepared to play the host as if no stigma of disgrace touched his guest.

He insisted that Monmouth remain with them until the old house in the Lange Voorhout should be ready to receive him. There was a good deal to see to there. The old Princess of Orange, William's grandmother, had lived in the house in stately magnificence, but for long enough, after her death, the rooms had remained empty. A great bustle and cleaning broke out in it, and so much new furniture ordered, it was obvious that Monmouth's banishment was to last for some time as he had foretold.

Meanwhile, his high spirits brought more gaiety to The House in the Wood. He charmed everyone, even the oldest and strictest of the courtiers. He seemed to charm even William. For when dance music stole softly through the ballroom in the long summer evenings, William was actually seen to dance, a thing he had not bothered about for many a year.

He danced quite well, but not nearly so well as his handsome cousin. When he had danced with Mary, he would hand her over to Monmouth, and then everyone drew aside to enjoy the grace of those two. Mary had given up dancing because William had. Now she renewed her youth, and William seemed quite pleased that she should do so. He would stand watching her, his eyes gravely approving. But Monmouth outshone them all, even Mary. She noticed that, disgraced or not, he always wore the insignia of the George which his father had given him.

When news of the favors shown him reached England, Mary received a letter from her father. The outraged Duke of York wrote that "it scandalizes all loyal and monarchical people here to know how well the Prince lives with and how civil he is to the Duke of Monmouth." Mary always wept easily, and she burst into tears as she read the letter. Then she went to find William and show it to him.

William read it calmly and only said, "I too have received a letter; from our uncle the King," and he handed it over to her.

She read it eagerly, and with growing alarm. It sounded very angry indeed. King Charles forbade his nephew to show Monmouth honor or even to receive him. The phrases used in the letter seemed strange and foreign to Mary who had never heard her good-humored uncle express himself in these terms before.

It was almost as if someone else had dictated the letter and even held the pen. . . .

"Are you going to do as he says?" she asked.

William shook his head. "He doesn't really want me to. He could never punish Monmouth; he loves him too well."

She still looked fearfully at the piece of paper in William's hand. "How do you know?"

"Look at the seal."

For a moment she did not understand. The red seal dangling from the letter by its ribbon was so familiar. It was the one her uncle invariably used. Then, suddenly she remembered.

"It is not——"

"It isn't the seal he took from his pocket and showed me. He means the letter to be disregarded."

"What then will you write to the King?"

"I shall write respectfully, saying his orders came too late for me to obey them. Having granted his son a house at The Hague and a guard of honor, I cannot disgrace myself and him by taking them away again."

So Monmouth began to rule the Court there, as he had ruled at St. James's. When autumn came, he hunted with

William. They went off together to hunt wild boar in the great forests of Guelderland, far from the tame woods about The Hague. When winter returned and the canals froze once more, Monmouth insisted upon teaching Mary to skate. He made her wear short skirts which scandalized the French Ambassador (he wrote back to France about them) and she didn't care who saw her moving inexpertly over the ice, falling and getting up with a laugh to try again.

And William watched quietly from the side lines. Well he knew that he had her heart. He could afford to ignore the light flirtation, the charming compliments paid to each other, the fun which meant nothing at all, but relieved the dullness of his own stodgy Court.

Then, about Christmas time, Monmouth suddenly disappeared. He was absent from a Court ball without any word of excuse. He did not appear to be at the house on the Lange Voorhout. Nobody knew where he was, not even William. Or did William perhaps guess? For when she asked him, he said, as usual, nothing at all.

As mysteriously as he had gone, he reappeared. Mary was skating, rather disconsolately, wishing he was there to see how well she could do figures now. Around her moved the citizens of The Hague, keeping a respectful distance from royalty, but nevertheless insisting upon enjoying themselves, too. Although she had made so much progress, Mary could not help envying the effortless way the Dutch skimmed over the ice as though they had been born to skates. None of the little boys and girls tumbled about as she had done. They curved and wheeled with a superior air. And even the middle-aged moved with a grace for which they were not especially renowned when walking on ordinary roads.

That man now, cutting through the crowd as though on wings . . . The next moment she saw it was Monmouth himself. He made straight for her, his face alight with happiness.

"Where in the world have you been?" She tried to sound angry, but couldn't manage it.

He slipped his hand under her arm and wheeled her off from the others so that he could speak privately in her ear. "Over to England. To see my father. He forgives me, Mary. He *knows* that, however foolish I might have been in joining with other men's plans, I would never suffer anyone to raise a hand against him!"

"Oh, why did you not tell us? We couldn't think——"

"How could I, when by the very going, I was disobeying His Majesty's command? What else could William have done but tried to stop me?"

"Yes, of course . . . I didn't think. . . ."

"Gibson got me a passage on a cargo boat crossing to Harwich. He loves contriving that sort of thing. I traveled as Mr. James Stuart; you would have laughed if you saw my traveling dress! Very sober; unlike me in fact. Nobody noticed me as I rode on a hired hack up to London——"

"How unusual for you, James!" Mary laughed out of sheer relief.

"Rather insulting, don't you think? But they weren't expecting to see the Protestant Duke, even at St. James's."

"You dared to enter St. James's?"

"Oh," he told her loftily, "I know the backstairs entrances as well as the front ones. I know just when and where to find my father alone. And that he could never resist my appeal to come home."

She was not surprised that his mission had been successful. He was always successful, especially with his doting father. "Yes, Mary," he was saying now, "I had only to avoid meeting *your* father, and all was sure to be well. Imagine the pleasure the Duke of York would have had in clapping me into prison for disobeying His Majesty's own orders!"

"The King has said you may return home?"

Monmouth nodded complacently. "He warmed up mightily as soon as he saw me. I think he had been missing me at Court. He told me to come back here and wait a little while longer, when he will revoke my exile and call me back. Only a little while longer!"

Chapter
Twelve

The beginning of the year 1685 saw a frozen stillness
lie over the whole of Holland. The snow had stopped.
The wind had fallen. Nature as well as Monmouth,
seemed to hold its breath, waiting. . . .

Frost stars sprinkled the windows of The House in the
Wood so that, first thing in the morning, one could
scarcely see out of them. Then, when the great stoves were
restoked and the frost patterns melted on the glass, one
could look out on a vast whiteness, stretching all the way
to the white and black woods beyond.

Mary took pity on the frozen and starving animals. She
carried a bag of crumbs tucked into her sable muff, and

when her sledge carried her over the snow, she would scatter the crumbs as she went. She took pity on Monmouth as well, in his impatient waiting. With the approval of William, she had the Orange Hall opened and prepared for dancing every night.

This is the finest of the rooms in the little palace and is lined with magnificent paintings, mostly portraits of members of the House of Orange. Some of them seemed to look down with astonishment at the gay scenes beneath them, particularly William the Silent, the taciturn sovereign; Prince Maurice the great soldier; and the childlike, still figure of William's mother, painted on her arrival in Holland.

Sometimes they looked down on theatricals instead. The French Ambassador, who had to be invited because of his rank, wrote home to Paris, more shocked than ever: The Princess of Orange played any sort of part, even the wildest, most skittish, and her husband said never a word! The Princess of Orange disgraced herself by dressing up as a peasant girl, a fishwife, or any other part she chose to take. The Princess of Orange had grown wild about dancing. After years of behaving in a seemly way and leaving such capering to her maids of honor, she had taken up dancing again, particularly with her cousin the disgraced Duke of Monmouth. . . .

Little did Mary care what was said of her, so long as she could help Monmouth to pass the month of waiting.

The nights might be short, thanks to music and dancing, but the days were long. The frost had killed the scent

for hunting, and he found little enough to do with himself
until it was dark once more, and the lights shining out
from The House in the Wood summoned him back
there.

For Richard Gibson, the days were long, too. He found
the Dutch stodgy and dull. He longed to be back in England and to taste properly cooked beef again. The Dutch
stews and omelettes sickened him. Their rich spices caught
at his throat and made him cough. As for driving out in
the bitter cold to spend night after night watching other
people dancing (for no woman was small enough to be his
partner with dignity, and he detested making a spectacle
of himself), he knew of other, better ways of spending the
evening.

There were inns and wine shops along the canals. When
the great chandeliers of The House in the Wood blazed
out into the snow beyond, their smoky lamps sent a glow-
ing welcome across the quays. Gibson was an abstemious
little man; he could make one glass of schnapps last a
whole evening. In any case, the strong Dutch liquor
caught at his throat, just as the strong Eastern spices
did.

But a glass of schnapps was his passport to warmth and
company. In particular, he felt most at home at The
House of the Trade Winds, a more modest establishment
than its name suggested, a mere slice of a brick house,
facing the Vijver. Inside it, however, he was sure to meet
seafaring men who spoke English. The Hague was only
two miles away from the coast and the little fishing village

of Scheveningen. And while the big ships that made regular passages across the North Sea were more apt to put in at Amsterdam, there was gossip to be picked up here, too, from fishermen returned from trips to the English seacoast, or from sailors visiting The Hague.

The frost still held. The mouths of the rivers were frozen, so that the trading ships could move neither out nor in. The dwarf was an Englishman, first and last. If he had to live abroad with his master, he made the best of it, but he longed to be back in England. His master, Monmouth, had told him about the King's promise of a recall at the end of a month. He had been counting the days ever since. Seven days made a week. Four weeks and a bit made a month.

The bit stretched to a week or more. The new crescent moon came, and grew and shrank again to a sliver. And still the summons did not come. It was the frost, of course. The great frost, that held ships and messages up on the Thames just as it did on the Scheldt. Why, there had been no new faces for weeks at The Trade Winds! No new gossip, just the same frequenters who lived in The Hague and were uncivilized enough to know no language but their own. . . .

Still, there had been news of a rescued fishing boat or two, put into Scheveningen lately. With luck, fresh company might turn up at The Trade Winds this night, the sixteenth of February. Soon after the Duke had driven off in his coach to spend the evening at The House in the Wood, Richard Gibson let himself out of the house on the

Lange Voorhout, into the still, cutting air.

There were many more canals threading The Hague then, than now. Many more little humpbacked bridges and slippery quays. It was dark too. Only an occasional lantern at some street corner told Gibson where he was. The new moon was too pale to be of much use and the stars though brilliant as diamonds, were as cold and useless.

The dwarf was thankful when he saw, beckoning toward him across the frozen Vijver the lantern outside the entrance to The Trade Winds. He almost ran across the little bridge toward that welcome light. The door was pulled to, because of the cold, but it would never be bolted against a customer. Gibson pushed it open and was immediately greeted and comforted by the rush of warm air and tobacco smoke from the room beyond.

The regulars looked up and nodded to him, then went on with their games of draughts or cards. The smoke was so thick, and the light from the coarse tallow candles so dim, Richard had difficulty at first in seeing where an empty place could be found. There was one table already occupied by two men, sailors by the look of them. Strangers, too, and with luck, just landed from the outside world.

Gibson swept off the plumed hat which looked so incongruous in this world of woolen or fur caps, and asked permission, in English, to seat himself. To his delight, the one man answered in English, while the other looked as though he understood it.

"More schnapps for these gentlemen!" The dwarf called out grandly. He loved making such a gesture, and besides, spirits generally loosened tongues. . . .

The more talkative of the two men was also the younger. He needed little encouragement to practice his broken English and say where he had come from. Tired of waiting for the weather to change, he and his mates had taken their small fleet of fishing boats right out into the North Sea. There a fierce storm would have finished them, had not an English trader rescued them and put them off at Scheveningen before battling on its way to Antwerp.

The dwarf nodded as he listened. This was the lot he had heard about. Now perhaps he could get some news, sailors' gossip even, about what was happening in England. The English trading ship must have sailed from a Devon port where the weather was milder. And London news trickled down even as far as Devon, give it time. . . .

They told him the news.

At first it stunned him. Then he did not believe it. At that, the older of the two fishermen grew grumpy and truculent. Why should be not believe it, pray? Was it not the talk of the whole British fleet, of everyone not cooped up with his ears stopped with frost?

The younger one spoke. Why (he asked slowly, in halting words), should the English ship have bothered to put them ashore instead of taking them on to Antwerp? Because there were messages, dispatches bearing the same news, in the hands of a grand gentleman (no sea legs though. Lord, how sick the man had been!) And *he* had

had to be landed, too. No doubt by tomorrow morning everyone would know if their words were true or not. . . .

The dwarf stared wildly about him. A few moments ago the cozy room, the bright copper pots, the smell of food, had spelled comfort. Now, suddenly, it had become a cage. The sort of place in which—if the news were true—he must take his ease forever, just as his master, the Duke, must forever look down upon foreign canals by day, and dance in a foreign palace, night after night. . . .

The Duke! He must hear the news at once. Gibson started to his feet, slamming down some money on the table as he did so. He said to the landlord urgently, "Where can I hire a horse?"

"For tomorrow morning? There's my nephew, he runs a livery stable——"

"No. For tonight!"

"For tonight?" The man stared at him, then shook his head. "I doubt if he'll have a mount fit to go after being out all day."

The dwarf caught hold of his sleeve. " 'Tis for no journey at all. Only two miles out of The Hague. He'll be back in the stable within an hour I promise you!"

The landlord hesitated. He wanted to oblige a good customer, and if the horse was wanted for only an easy journey, no harm would be done.

"Wait here, Mijnheer," he said at last, "while I go the few steps to my nephew's and see what he has to say."

The door opened and shut, letting in a sharp air, then cutting it off again. The dwarf waited, staring unseeingly at the game being played on a draught board under his nose. He seemed to be following the moves, but was aware of nothing until he heard, above the rumble of voices, the clip-clop of a horse's hoofs being led over the cobbles toward the door.

He flew to the door, struggling into his thick leather coat as he went. There stood the trees by the Dyver with the stars above them, and there stood the horse. Not much of an animal for speed, and already worked pretty hard that day. But better than a long, trudging walk over snow and ice, with the risk of arriving at the palace after the lights had been put out. . . .

He swung himself into the saddle and cantered off. He knew, by now, all the short cuts through the old city, and how to emerge from it on the side nearest to the Wood. He did not know that another horseman had taken the route before him already. It would have made no difference if he had.

The foresters had made well-defined paths through the Wood so that huntsmen could ride down them easily. Gibson knew those paths. He knew, too, that few trusted themselves to the Wood at night. Landmarks looked different under the moon, and though on the whole the Dutch were law-abiding, there was always the risk of being held up at pistol point by some deserter from the army. The other horseman had been told this, and had ridden by the longer, more open route. Gibson didn't care about danger. He rode his horse right into the Wood.

How silent it was, how like a dream! Perhaps the terrible news he had heard in the Inn was a dream too. But even if it was, yet in a dream he must find his master and tell him. An owl called above his head. He could see the wavering shadow of the bird crossing a clear patch of snow. Then the clearing vanished behind him, the trees closed in again, and he could only glimpse starlight between their branches, here and there.

He felt as if he were carrying on his own back all the terrible news in the world. Compared with it, his master was living in paradise. It was a false paradise, built of false hopes. Why was he hurrying so, to shatter it? Because it was shattered already, and he must be at his master's side when the news came.

The trees spread out more thinly again. Now he had reached the edge of the Wood, and could see the palace, and the lights pouring out of its windows, and hear the beat of the music inside. He rode the horse gently over what, in summer, would be flower beds and little paths, but was now only a waste of snow. The stone steps were like pillars of snow. The elaborate pattern of tiles in the courtyard, before the main entrance, was slippery with frozen snow.

Gibson dismounted and led his horse across it. Now the music sounded more clearly. The sentry boxes were empty; it was far too cold for the guards to stand there on duty. The footmen who should have guarded the inner doors seemed to have vanished. The dwarf decided to go to the lighted windows and call someone's attention through them.

There was only a small gap between the curtains of the windows of the room in which the ball was being held. Pressing his nose to the glass, he tried to peer into the room. But the music had grown louder, the swirling throng of dancers passed and repassed so quickly, it was impossible for anyone to pause long enough to catch a glimpse of his anxious face, or to hear the tapping his fist made on the glass.

"A pest on dancing!" he exclaimed angrily and began to walk farther along the terrace. At its farther end was a glass door. Gibson saw that here, too, the curtains inside the room had not been drawn quite together. With luck someone might be there who would hear his knocking. . . .

It was an oddly bare room for a palace. There was hardly anything in it but a desk, and an upright chair and a man sitting on the chair writing. His head was bent down over the paper, so that Gibson could not see who it was. Cold and angry and afraid, the dwarf battered peremptorily on the glass door.

The man sprang up and came toward it with two strides. Gibson found himself looking straight into the eyes of the Prince of Orange, with only a thin pane of glass between them.

The Prince wrenched the door open. "What the devil——"

The dwarf tumbled into the room. "I came to find my master—to give him bad news! But I can't get in, and I can't make them hear——"

William bolted the door again, and led the trembling little man toward the warmth of the stove. "If your news is from England, I know it already."

The dwarf caught hold of the edge of the desk to steady himself. "Then it's true that the King is dead. . . . I had hoped maybe it was only a false rumor . . ."

William had seated himself behind the desk again. With his eyes on the paper he held in his hand, he said, "This intelligence only reached me an hour ago. His Majesty died of a fit of apoplexy on the seventh of this month. It is now the sixteenth. We have to thank the weather for preventing us from getting word until now."

"He promised to send for the Duke in a month——"

"King Charles will never summon anyone again." The Prince picked up his pen as a hint that he was busy and the audience was over. But now anger shook Richard Gibson. Recklessly he exclaimed, "And you have known it this past hour while the Ball goes on and my master still dances!"

There was a pause. Gibson fully expected to be ordered to prison for his insolence. But the Prince only glanced at the clock on the wall before answering quietly, "I was averse to spoiling his pleasure. He will not dance again for some time. I had given them until midnight——"

The clock began to strike. It gave twelve strokes, echoed faintly outside by the one in the stable belfry. When the last stroke had chimed, William rose from the desk and said, "Now it is time the dancing stopped. You may follow me."

The thin man and the little man left the room together. William walked back along the corridor toward the room where they were dancing. He entered an anteroom next to it, and signed to the footmen to throw open the communicating doors.

Instantly the music burst out, loud in their ears. The sudden blaze of lights stabbed Gibson's eyeballs after his long ride through the dark. He blinked once or twice, while the dancers stopped in motion, like mechanical dolls run down, and the music stopped.

Mary and her cousin stood poised in astonishment. Their right arms still remained in an arc above their heads, their hands joined in the figure of the dance. Mary's face suddenly glowed at the sight of William coming to join them. But Monmouth saw William's expression. And a cold shadow of premonition touched him where he stood, with the Princess' hand in his.

Chapter
Thirteen

On April 23, 1685, James II was crowned King of
Great Britain and Ireland, and Mary Beatrice, his gentle
wife, was now Queen.

Monmouth shut himself up in his own house, mourning
his father. He had loved him, and had lived under his
protection so long, he scarcely realized at first that the new
King would be his implacable enemy. If Charles had only
lived a week or two longer; if he had summoned his son
home sooner; if. . . .

The dwarf slept outside Monmouth's room each night
and scarcely left it each day. He knew when the handsome,
proud man broke down and shed tears as soon as he

thought himself alone. He hid the bills which began to pour in, and prevented Monmouth's creditors from getting near his master to trouble him. As long as Monmouth was still the favorite son of the King of England, he had got as much credit as he liked. Now that sheltering hand was removed, everyone suddenly wanted their accounts paid. At once.

One morning, soon after the new King's accession, a message came from William, saying he wanted to see his cousin. Monmouth had lately shrunk from seeing anyone but Gibson, who took the message to him.

The Duke knew what it meant at once. He said with a bitter smile, "Now I shall receive my congé from the Prince. He cannot afford to offend the new King."

James Monmouth entered his coach and drove off to The House in the Wood. He was dressed in deep mourning, which only set off the pale Stuart features, and he wore proudly, almost flauntingly, the George, the decoration his father had given him.

William received him in the little bare room Richard Gibson had been in a few nights before. Monmouth glanced around quickly, but Mary was not there. He had hardly expected her to be. He knew already what William was going to say; and could guess how hard Mary had pleaded with her husband not to say it.

William gave a short bow. "I fear, my cousin, that the death of King Charles has altered your prospects here in Holland."

Well, at least he had called him cousin. Monmouth said

shortly and coldly, "You mean you want me to go?"

For once, the Prince of Orange seemed not so sure of himself as usual. "I am in a difficult situation. Your father asked me privately to be your friend. I obeyed him. But I cannot afford to displease the new King. You were his rival to the throne——"

"I *am* his rival to the throne!" the Duke interrupted proudly.

It was a mistake. The other's tone became equally cold as he said, "I would advise you to drop such pretensions; they are only foolishness. I still want to help you, but only so long as you make no friction between myself and our uncle in England."

"Then you cannot help me at all!"

"Oh yes I can." William trifled with some papers lying on his desk. "This is a confidential report of your—financial difficulties, Cousin. Forgive me if I have seemed to pry into them. But since you may be leaving Holland soon, I must see that your debts are settled. I do this gladly. And if a sum of money to start you elsewhere is of any use . . ."

Monmouth's face flushed crimson with anger. Then the color ebbed from it as he realized his position. There would be no more funds smuggled across the North Sea to him from a doting father. He was penniless.

He said shortly, "Thank you, Cousin. Beggars cannot be choosers."

Then William made an unusual move, for him. He took a step nearer his cousin and laid a hand on his shoulder. The two Stuart faces were now near together. And on

William's there was an expression of sympathy and sad-
ness, which few people ever saw.

"I like you, James. We represent different sides of the
same medal. You have all the charm, the qualities which—
which I envy. But I am not so small a man as to bear you a
grudge for that. Won't you believe that I want to help
you?"

"Perhaps." But his cousin's tone was still bitter. "You
are offering to help me with money. What do you propose
that I should do with the rest of my life?"

"You are an excellent soldier. Make that your career.
Not under me. King James would hardly approve of that!
But why not ask the Emperor of Austria for a command?
He would welcome your sword."

Monmouth moved restlessly about the room. "How
long do you give me here?" he asked abruptly.

"I would not presume to set a period to your conveni-
ence. The house here had perhaps better be handed over
very shortly—say, in a week. I dare say when the new King
hears I have requested it back, he will not trouble himself
about your precise movements, once you have left my capital."

The two cousins looked into each other's eyes; understood one another. William made a sign that the interview
was over. James Monmouth, with his hand on the door,
turned to ask, for the first time diffident, "May I say good-
by to Mary?"

"She is not here. Before I sent for you, I suggested that
she should leave for Guelderland. She was very upset by

your change of fortune. It is best to avoid tears."

"Yes, I remember you always hated them," Monmouth commented dryly, as he left the room.

The Province of Guelderland is famous for its forests and sport, which was why William had bought a small hunting lodge there some two years before. Mary had been enthusiastic when he first told her of his plan to build a new, magnificent chateau near the old hunting lodge where they might stay until the building was completed.

She had felt, then, that in this remote, wild district, she would have William more to herself. Now, she knew she had been virtually banished here, to be out of the way while Monmouth's future was settled without her.

The great forest held the cold more tightly than did the smaller woods about The Hague. The little old hunting lodge was primitive compared with the comfort of William's palaces. The trees pressed about it more closely, too. The rooms were small and dark, and their windows must be kept carefully shut because of the wreaths of damp rising out of the moat which contained the old building.

Last year the erection of the new palace had begun, and Mary herself had laid the foundation stone. William had rejoiced in drawing up plans and exercising his talent for architecture. It had been warm summer. He had left the planning of the gardens to Mary. She had found it amusing to order a maze and see the young hedges laid out in bewildering patterns. The Avenue of Ceres was a charming invention too. It entailed planting a double row of trees with a strip of turf running between them like a green carpet, up to the statue of Ceres, the Goddess of the Harvest. This would make a pleasing vista, seen from the windows of the new palace, once the trees were grown tall enough.

But nothing was finished, and the snow had stopped all building and planting. It was difficult to fill in the days. Her attendants complained of cold, boredom and open wood fires instead of comfortable stoves. Het Loo had only been meant to accommodate hunting parties for a night or two at a time. True, there were many fine hunting castles spread through the Forest which stretched for thirty square miles. And the great families of Holland, the Bentincks, the Keppels, would come into residence even during the winter, to enjoy the wild-boar hunts in which William delighted.

Mary's sitting room was in one of the pepper-pot towers of the old castle. Its window stared straight over the moat into the forest. Each evening there was just a moment when the red sun, sinking behind the trees, caught the leaded-glass panes of her window and set them on fire. She would move to the window seat then, to get the last of the light for the book she was reading, or the tiny, delicate painting on ivory she was intent on finishing.

She was sitting there when she heard the hunting horn blow faintly through the Forest. It was the note used for a kill. She raised her head sharply, listening.

Her lady in waiting exclaimed, "I wonder Count Bentinck ventures to hunt so near to your Highness' walls. It is not respectful."

The tops of the trees had already swallowed up the sun and the print of her book became blurred. Mary rose to go nearer the fire and the candles. The horn had stopped blowing. But now the two women heard another sound directly beneath the window. The sound of horsemen riding across the wooden bridge over the moat. She stepped back quickly and looked down.

It was William escorted by Count Bentinck and some other huntsmen. Mary flew from the room to receive him. He had suddenly seen his way (so he told her before the others) to spare a day or two for his favorite sport. Reaching Bentinck's Castle of Amerongen late last night, he had spent the night there so as to start off early next morning. They had killed three wild boar, and now he was tired and hungry. . . .

Indeed he looked tired. Mary knew how extreme cold generally brought on an attack of asthma or bronchitis. She wondered at his choosing such weather to hunt in. But, as always, his comparative silence imposed a like silence on her. At least, she did not ask questions.

He had enjoyed his sport, but sure enough, the damp cold under the trees, added to the miasma from the moat, gave him a fit of coughing that evening which nearly choked him. He had to sit up, propped against pillows, half the night. Not for the first time Mary wondered at the iron spirit which drove his frail body to physical exertions too great for it. But, watching him and ministering to him as she could, she suppressed the questions she wanted to ask, as so often she had to suppress others for fear of offending him, or of getting no answer at all.

In the early hours of the morning he fell asleep. Mary hoped he would sleep late, but she was sipping her own morning chocolate when he appeared, dressed, booted to go out, looking as impassive as ever.

"When you are ready, my dear," he said, "we might walk to the new building, to see how things are getting on."

Naturally, in this weather, they had not got on at all. But she guessed he had something to say which he wanted to say out of doors, without eavesdroppers. Bentinck and his party had ridden away again after supper last night. The beginnings of the new palace of Het Loo were only a short walk away. But Mary drove there in a little basket carriage drawn by one old pony whose pace was so slow, William could easily walk by her side.

Only the foundations were laid, and they were almost invisible under the snow. "Here," William drew a semicircle with his stick, "we shall have a half-moon of pillars, a Gloriette such as the Emperor has erected at Schönbrunn. It will be a sufficient way off from the palace to afford a ——"

"William, please tell me. Where is our cousin Monmouth?"

"——vista." William finished the sentence coolly, adding, "I don't know."

"You don't——" She scarcely understood him, he was so abrupt.

"I withdrew the residence I had lent him, together with my official support. Your father knows that. It ought to satisfy him. Monmouth is no longer living at The Hague. What business is it of mine where he has gone to?"

She understood him now. Thankfulness, and affection for William made the tears come into her eyes. "You mean, he is still safe in Holland? You haven't ordered him to leave the country?"

He gave his crooked smile at her. His nose looked bigger than ever. "Why should I if he has already left? Even King James can't prove that I'm harboring him, so long as I can't tell where he is!"

It was in the Stadtholder's power to have every prominent person followed and reported upon. So William as Stadtholder was deliberately shutting his eyes to Monmouth's whereabouts. He was saying now, "King James has already asked for information regarding him. Was it not fortunate that I couldn't give it?"

"You have a generous heart!"

"Besides," William went on evenly, "we must not forget that Monmouth is, in one sense, your rival. You are officially acknowledged to be the next heir to the English Crown. To act otherwise than we have done, would look like taking Monmouth's pretensions too seriously."

Mary said nothing. For some reason she felt disappointed.

William pointed with the cane he carried toward the Avenue of Ceres. "That was a happy thought, my love. Who knows what may happen in England before the trees grow much higher?"

 Chapter
Fourteen

Over in England, the new King proceeded to put his foot in it again and again, just as his brother had foretold. He took no account of the almost hysterical fears of his people lest papacy should be imposed on them once more against their will. He attended Mass publicly in one of the chapels of Protestant Westminster Abbey. Monks with rosaries in their hands appeared in their habits in the streets of London. The Protestant Bishop of London was suspended from his office. And in even the academic field, the King managed to quarrel with the universities of both Oxford and Cambridge by trying to interfere with their traditions and rules.

Over in Holland, William watched and said nothing. It was true that his wife was now the admitted heiress to her father. She was given special honors and "served on the knee." But James preserved his cold silence toward her. Only Anne's letters told her how things were going at home.

Mary had returned, as usual, to Honselaarsdijk in time for the tulips. She made no effort to find out where Monmouth was. She knew it was safer for him if she remained ignorant, and so could not inform anyone of his whereabouts. The Van Tol tulip bloomed as usual. The bulbs had multiplied so that a whole bed was aflame with its color. Presently, she thought, I should like to go by water through the fields of tulips, as soon as the air gets a little warmer. . . .

She had spoken her thought out loud, and William answered unexpectedly, "Not presently. Now. And I will accompany you. I have business in Utrecht; someone to see there."

They traveled by coach to Utrecht instead of canal. The slow progress of a barge was too much for William's impatient spirit, and besides traveling by water was bad for his chest. Yet the bulb fields shone just as brightly on either side of the road as on either side of the water. It was a fresh spring morning with a sky of robin's-egg blue. The air was so clear that the spire of Utrecht Cathedral rose up before them when they were yet many miles from the town.

It looked so different, now that the snow was gone! The

Oude Gracht encircling the town was now filled with clear
water instead of ice. William had formed his plan unexpectedly and had especially desired that their visit should
be as private as possible. Only a small deputation waited
on them therefore, at the entrance to the town. The citizens had not been told of their coming, so there were few
people standing by to hear William ask to be taken to the
lodging of Dr. Wallace.

The English, or rather, Scotch name startled Mary.
Who was this Doctor Wallace of whom William had never
spoken before? The coachman was given directions and
the coach turned off the main street, into a network of
shabby little streets and lanes bordering the canals.

It stopped in front of a small house, painted dazzling
white with green shutters clamped primly back. A maid-
servant was scrubbing the step. She raised her head as the
coach wheels rattled over the stones toward the house, and
then jumped up when it stopped. Although the girl was
dressed in a coarse blue gown with a drugget apron to
protect it, she gave an impression of fineness. She curtseyed, and the curtsey was not the quick bob of the working woman greeting her superiors; it was oddly graceful
and dignified.

There was something puzzling about her. And when
both Mary and William had left the coach, William became puzzling too. For instead of giving his usual curt nod
in recognition of the girl's greeting, he actually bowed,
then turned to his wife, saying with an odd look, "Pray say
something kind to Miss Wallace. She deserves it."

Then he turned back quickly to the girl, asking, "Is your father at home? I am the Stadtholder. I want a word with him."

The girl who now called herself Grizel Wallace, gestured to them to enter the house before her. "I will go and fetch my father, your Highness. He is attending to a patient farther up the street."

It was a very small house and a very small parlor, poorly furnished but scrupulously clean. There was the usual painted furniture of such a place. But while they waited, Mary saw one or two incongruous objects lying about. A gentleman's sword propped up in one corner; a gold snuff box lying on a table, and two silver candlesticks, battered and thin but bearing a coat of arms. And, in one corner of the room, a harpsichord.

William tapped impatiently on the lid of the harpsichord until he heard the sound of footsteps in the street outside. The girl, Grizel, who looked about eighteen or nineteen years old, came back into the room followed closely by her father. Mary saw a tall, middle-aged bearded man with the severe and saddened expression she had noticed in the strangers who had been slipping unobtrusively into Holland of late.

William turned to her, "My dear, let me present this gentleman, who goes by the name of Doctor Wallace. But I believe you will keep his secret if I tell you that at home in Scotland he is more generally known as Sir Patrick Hume of Marchmont."

Sir Patrick kissed Mary's hand. She was reminded of the

somewhat uncouth Scots courtiers at King Charles's court when he spoke. There was the same accent, but also the same dignity and pride of race.

"I have to thank the Stadtholder for sheltering us. At home we are passing through difficult times."

Mary said, "Do you practice here as a doctor of medicine? Are you that as well?"

The grave man smiled. "I have knocked about the world, your Highness. I have learned many trades, including that of the chirurgeon. I can keep my family by that employment until—better times come."

William said in a low voice, "His estates were confiscated because of the part he played in the recent rebellions." He turned again to Doctor Wallace. "You have means of receiving news, still, I believe?"

The other was silent a moment or two. It was as if he tried to make up his mind whether the Prince was asking him to betray himself and his friends. At last he said, speaking clearly and distinctly, "That is so, your Highness. My compatriots make their way over here for protection, and they keep us *au courant*. Also, a few of my loyal tenants find means to write. I trust that your Highness will not inquire by what means they do this."

"That is no business of mine." William made an abrupt gesture. "I wish to know if there is any truth in the rumor that the Earl of Argyll is planning yet another rebellion of your tumultuous people?"

"I believe it is true, your Highness. And if——"

William stopped him suddenly. "Your 'if' is impossible.

Even if I had the power, I would never give aid to rebels
against their sovereign. . . . But I would like to learn more
from you, for my own satisfaction. Can we talk privately
somewhere?"

The man who called himself Doctor Wallace looked
irresolute once more. He seemed to be weighing the
danger of confiding in the Prince against that of withholding knowledge from the man who had the power to close
the doors of Holland to them all.

William, watching him, added, "I am not concerning
myself in the quarrel. But I have reasons for being interested. You must trust me, I think."

"Come into another room, Sir. I know little enough
myself, and cannot implicate even Argyll since you know
already he is concerned."

The two men left the room together. Grizel smiled
shyly at the Princess. "Can I offer you some refreshment,
Madam?"

She was such a pretty girl, with the open, sweet looks of
Joanna, yet with much more character and poise. Her skin
was clear with the fairness made by Scotch mists and rain.
Her hands were well shaped with long, tapering fingers.
Mary grieved to see such aristocratic hands reddened and
roughened by hard work.

Grizel saw the glance and put her hands quickly behind
her back. "I am sorry your Highness saw me scrubbing the
steps. Sorry, but not ashamed."

Mary liked the girl better than ever. "Perhaps you cannot afford a maid of all work?"

She knew, in the instant of speaking, that this was no place for leaving gold pieces unobtrusively on a table. The money would be instantly resented and returned. She hoped her tones had sounded mere kindly interest.

Grizel flushed. "Ordinarily we do. But my father has friends newly come over from Scotland with nothing but what they stand up in. We have been trying to help them a little."

"I see." Pity for her could no longer be suppressed. "But have you no distractions—no pleasures? I hope you have some time for them at least!"

The girl hesitated, then glanced toward the harpsichord. "My father likes me to sing to him in the evenings."

Mary had noticed a page of manuscript lying on the lid. She walked over and picked it up. It was the manuscript of a song. She could read music swiftly, but the tune seemed unknown to her, and the words almost unintelligible. "Who composed this?" she asked. "What is its name?"

Two dimples appeared in Grizel's cheeks. "I wrote it myself, your Highness. And it's called 'Werena' my heart licht I wad dee.' "

Then she smiled mischievously at the sight of Mary's embarrassment. "We speak another sort of English from what your Highness would be accustomed to in London. . . . Shall I translate?"

"Please. And sing it afterward."

"Och, the words just mean, If my heart wasn't light, I would die. I wrote it when I felt that way."

She began to play and sing the song. It had the ring of an old ballad, or a simple love song, but it was Grizel's own, and it has survived, in her country, until this day. She sang:

"When bonnie young Johnnie came over the sea,
He vowed he saw nothing so lovely as me;
He gave me gold rings, and many braw things,
And werena' my heart licht I wad dee."

Grizel's voice, sweet and rounded, died in the room, and the plucked sound of the harpsichord faded, too. Mary thought: This girl would be as faithful as Joanna, but more companionable for she has talent and breeding. Aloud, because her thoughts were otherwise occupied, she said what had come into her head. "What does braw mean?"

Again the girl laughed aloud. It was such young, fresh laughter, Mary felt like joining in too. "And your Highness a Stuart! Oh, pardon, I should not have said that. But the word means fine."

Just then a young man entered the parlor directly from the street. "Entertaining visitors at this hour, Sister? I thought I heard music."

"Be respectful, Patrick. This is the Princess of Orange."

The young man colored and bowed very low. "Forgive my intrusion, Madam. I had no idea——"

"Of course not." Mary saw he was handsome and carried himself with an air. But the air masked desperate shabbiness and a pinched anxiety sad to see on so young a face. She was about to say something to him when William re-entered the room. So she presented the boy to her husband instead.

William gave Patrick Hume his usual keen glance. "You are old enough to help your family's fortunes," he said bluntly. "What do you do with your time? I hope you don't waste it in hanging idly about."

The young man's father laid his hand on his son's shoulder. "Patrick's no waster, Sir. He picks up what he can by teaching English, although he is cut out for a soldier rather than a scholar."

"So?" The Prince's heavy Dutch accent seemed accentuated although he spoke English with absolute correctness. Used to summing up men, he seemed satisfied with what he saw of Patrick Hume. "If he prefers a uniform, let him wear mine. He is still too young to serve in camp. But I shall appoint him one of my Royal Corps of Guards."

"Your Highness!" Patrick's face shone with joy, and even his stern father looked gratified. The Royal Corps of Guards was composed of young men of noble family. It gave considerable prestige and meant that each member was under the Prince's own protection.

Grizel cried out, "Oh Patrick, you'll look gey handsome in the uniform! Ye'll be wearing lace ruffles, too! I can starch lace. I'll see to them for you!"

They escorted their royal visitors out to the street where the coach still stood waiting. But the street was no longer empty. Mary noticed a little knot of men, Scotsmen she now knew from their clothes, standing with their backs to the canal. They took off their hats silently as they watched the Stuart Princess, who came from their own long line of kings, drive off again.

As they passed through the town on their way home, William said abruptly, "That girl is a heroine. Before they left Scotland, she hid her father in the family vaults near their village, and went alone, after dark, each night, to take him food!"

"What had Doctor—Sir Patrick done?"

"Stuck to his religion, chiefly." William gave her a grim smile. "And thus rebelled against King Charles. He was in safety, abroad, when he heard of a friend being implicated in the Rye House Plot. Believing that he could get him off, he returned to give evidence at the trial. He has barely escaped the second time with his life."

The Rye House Plot. Mary, stung to remembrance, asked quickly, "Are there to be more—reprisals? Did Sir Patrick say the Earl of Argyll really intended marching against my father?"

"His rebellion seems pretty well under way. I don't believe it will succeed. The army is still loyal to your father. And trained troops will always win the day against Argyll's untrained followers."

Now they were through the town and out on the flat roads running between the fields. A layer of sand blown in from the sea softened the roadway under the iron wheels of the coach so that William's voice came again with a sudden loud clearness.

"I am only afraid of what Monmouth may be encouraged to do. He may not share my opinion about Argyll's chances of success. Monmouth has everything else except good judgment. That, he never possessed."

 **Chapter**
Fifteen

From the deepest melancholy, Richard Gibson found his spirits rising again. He had shared Monmouth's feelings of despair at the death of the King. Nothing lay in front of them both, it seemed, but permanent exile abroad. And he knew, too, that the Duke was heartbroken at losing his father.

But when the ice floes melted and the first green appeared in the fields, it seemed as if his master had found some secret hope. He laid off his mourning, and Gibson happily did the same. Black was a pesky color anyway! And they both saw company again. Strange gentlemen turned up at the village inn where they had taken refuge

as being more inconspicuous and hidden than town lodg-
ings. Some of the gentlemen were Dutch. Others spoke
English but with the rough accents of the Scotch.

Gibson was banished from his master's room on these
occasions. One evening, in great secrecy, a tall man with
cold blue eyes was received, and Gibson noticed that the
Duke received him with more deference than he was
usually in the habit of giving. But the dwarf was dismissed
as usual. And when he was summoned again, the room was
empty and there was only the sound of a horse's hoofs
galloping toward the sea.

The village stood among the dunes, with the gray line
of the sea against the horizon. The small fishing harbor
was half a mile off, and Gibson, strolling toward it to kill
time until the Duke should have finished with the
stranger, had noticed a larger ship than usual lying, full
sail, ready to put off. He now suspected that the gentleman had been brought ashore from it. When he saw
Monmouth again, he was sure of it.

"I'll trust you with a secret." The Duke smiled affectionately at his faithful servant. "That was the Earl of
Argyll."

Gibson's mouth opened. "But—but——"

"Aye. I know. He's in trouble with King James at
present and it would embarrass the Prince of Orange to
receive him. So his visit to me has to be kept very secret, as
I warned you."

"Has his Lordship been in this country long, then?"

"Not longer than to talk with me here. Our fortunes are

very much entwined, Richard. They are rising like twin
stars, together."

Monmouth's whole manner had changed. His eyes
sparkled, and he spoke with a sort of feverish gaiety.
"That man, by raising his finger can raise a whole army!
D'ye know what a Highland Chief is, Richard? He's Head
of the Campbells, the greatest of all; the Macallum
Mohr!"

For the first and last time Richard Gibson experienced
a twinge of fear. His master's manner made him uneasy,
but only for the moment. He was too pleased to see the
Duke raised out of his melancholy to care what had done
it. But he wondered at Argyll's visit and at his secret coming and going. A little later, when he went to the inn door
to smoke his pipe, he saw that the great ship out in the
harbor had gone. . . .

It was shortly after this, that Monmouth announced
they must go to Amsterdam. They had hitherto avoided
large cities and public places. Monmouth had disregarded
his cousin's advice about enlisting in the Austrian army. It
had been wiser for them therefore, to lie low lest overzeal-
ous persons reported their presence to the Prince of
Orange and forced him to issue an order of banishment.

Gibson was a bold little man, but his heart was in his
mouth as they stole into the great city under cover of dark.
Here was the real heart of Holland. It was the commercial
capital where the merchant princes lived and conducted
their business. Here the great East India Company had its
head offices in a magnificent old house facing the water,

with the company's coat of arms sculptured over the door-
way. And here was the largest Jewish Quarter in that part
of Europe. They were wealthy merchants, too, but their
trade was in gold. They lent it out, and financed ventures
of which they approved. They walked the streets of the
city quietly and unmolested, their high turban head-
dresses or high fur caps marking them out from the other
citizens around them.

Gibson found himself tingling with excitement as the
boat slid through the water gate and entered the back
ways of the city. Although born a countryman, he had
lived most of his life in towns and at Court. The quietude
of the little Dutch village had bored him to extinction.
But now, even through the darkness, he could feel the
heartbeat of Amsterdam with its crowded streets and its
wealth and its vigorous life. And he revived as a plant
revives when someone pours water over it.

The boat stopped at one of the quays of the Heeren-
gracht, or Gentleman's Canal. Here stood the tall brick
houses of the chief merchants, each with its huge loft
under the pointed gables and its iron hook and chain by
which to lift up cargo to store in the loft. Monmouth's
servants were already taking their trunks out of the boat,
so it appeared that they were to stay in this house. And as
soon as the noise of their arrival was heard, the door flew
open hospitably.

Its owner stood there, grave in black velvet and golden
chains. He bowed deeply to the Duke, who gave him his
hand. Gibson trotted in after them, amazed at the splen-

dor of the building once one got behind its severe façade. Rich tapestries hung on the walls, fine Oriental rugs lay, Dutch fashion, across the heavy oak tables. And—what was even more important to the dwarf,—the spicy smells of a good supper wafted themselves through the house.

A number of other gentlemen stood behind their host. One or two were Jewish merchants by their dress. They went in to supper immediately, and the dwarf noticed how the shrewd eyes of the Dutchmen fixed themselves steadily on the face of the Duke, as though striving to read what character and purpose might lie behind his light-hearted charm.

Yet nothing was said to enlighten Gibson, until the end of the meal. Then Monmouth rose from his seat, holding a glass of wine in his hand.

"I call on you gentlemen to drink a toast. Success to all Merchant Adventurers!"

The merchants drank gravely without enthusiasm. Or so it seemed to Richard Gibson, carried away by his master's excitement. He was beginning now to have an inkling of the adventure lying before them. He was sure of it, when, after supper, the visitors dispersed. Gibson, examining a picture in the hall, stood unnoticed while two of them spoke to each other in low voices.

One was a rich Jew such as a famous citizen of Amsterdam, Rembrandt the painter, had loved to portray. The lamp from the ceiling caught the rich folds of his head-dress and glinted on the heavy gold chains fastening his cloak. His companion was a Christian, a well-known member of the Dutch East India Company, more soberly dressed.

He was saying, "I have lent him ten thousand gulden for the venture, win or lose."

The Jew answered, "It is not too much for a crown."

Then they all went away. And the dwarf kept his counsel, asked no questions, but noted how often his master visited the marine stores down by the quays and gunsmiths' shops; and was not surprised when at last Monmouth, taking him into his confidence, told him what was planned.

"I have bought a ship with the money loaned by some good gentlemen here. I have found recruits too, among some of the exiles my uncle has driven abroad. I wait only to hear of when Argyll engages the King's troops in the north. That's the moment for us to land in the south and win England!"

The dwarf nodded his head. He had been sure that something of this sort was in the wind. He asked a blunt question: "How many recruits?"

Monmouth looked discomposed for an instant. "Why— only one hundred and fifty for a start. But the moment we land there will be no difficulty about raising an army, I assure you! Argyll says the whole country, from north to south, is sick of King James's new measures. We shall land at Lyme, in Dorsetshire, where the people——"

"Supposing the Prince of Orange stops us?"

Monmouth burst out laughing. "Stop the means to put his wife on the throne? No, he's playing ignorance. That's why he hasn't bothered to seek us out and chivy me off to Vienna. He wants me to pull his chestnuts out of the fire for him!"

Gibson looked puzzled. "But I thought your Grace would be King!"

A strange expression flitted over the other's face for a moment. He said slowly, "The Princess of Orange is the next heir. I am proud to forward her cause. But if the people should insist upon me . . ."

After that conversation it seemed to Richard Gibson that everything went very quickly. They left Amsterdam as they had come, unobtrusively and at night. It was summer now, and the North Sea was blue and quiet. Only a small shore wind rustled the grasses on the sand dunes. Unregarded, they sailed out to where the great ship waited. The hundred and fifty recruits cheered from the decks as the Duke came on board. Then the anchor was lifted, and they sailed away.

It was the morning of May 24, 1685. They were becalmed for a while, and once or twice had to alter course to avoid a British warship. But at last, on June 11, Richard Gibson saw his native land again. There it lay, the Dorset coast, green and glimmering. Not like the grim rocks of his own north country, but for all that, England and home.

They were rowed ashore in small boats to find that that whole coast had caught the whisper of the Duke's coming already. Eager, expectant faces lined the shore, and a great cheer went up when the Protestant Duke was glimpsed at last. They were simple people, those Dorset countrymen, but they had long, long memories. They remembered the tales of Bloody Mary's reign and thought he had come to save them from the terrors of that time.

"God Save Our Protestant King!" they cried, throwing up their hats in the air. And James Monmouth waved his plumed hat toward them and smiled his enchanting smile, and pretended he had not heard the words. . . .

A band of young girls strewed flowers in his path as he entered the town. Every hour more recruits poured in until his ragged, untrained army reached the proportions he had boasted it would. True, the men who promised to fight for him had had no training, but surely enthusiasm would outweigh that? They came from even as far away as the midlands to fight for King Monmouth, as they now insisted on calling him.

And Monmouth, seeing that their enthusiasm was personal and for him, carried away by the adoration, the flower-strewn streets, the banners woven with a crown above his name, at last called himself King, too. On first landing he had issued a Proclamation against King James. Now, at Taunton in Somerset, on June 20 he proclaimed himself King of Great Britain and Ireland. . . .

But London paid no attention. Nobody came from there to join King Monmouth's army, and that caused the first chill apprehension to smite Mr. Gibson. He did not like it. It meant that the reigning King had his capital firmly under control.

Then, suddenly, came bad news from Scotland. The Earl of Argyll's rebellion had failed. He himself had been taken prisoner. Ten days after Monmouth had proclaimed himself King, the man who was to have been his chief supporter was publicly executed at Edinburgh. Bad news always travels quickly. The dwarf now shuddered when he heard this. What use to Argyll had been all those proud titles? He might have been the Macallum Mohr (whatever that meant), but King James had struck him down just the same.

And if this venture failed, too . . . Gibson's mind refused to accept the parallel. An earl was an earl certainly. But his master was the son of a king. Surely one did not execute king's sons, no matter what they had done!

Having settled matters in the north, the King's troops marched south at last. It was a trained, professional army, and it met Monmouth's ill-equipped, untrained men at a place called Sedgemoor. Monmouth himself was a brilliant soldier, but he could do nothing without properly tempered tools. And he was opposed by the finest commander in Britain, Sarah Jennings' husband, Colonel Churchill.

Those two men, who had often danced and laughed together at the court of King Charles, now faced each other grimly. And Monmouth lost. The dwarf, who was no good at fighting, watched anxiously from the roof of a farmhouse, while the battle rolled this way and that, and then, quite suddenly, became a rout. He saw the countrymen of the Duke's army break and fly for their lives. He heard their death cries as they were struck down. And then came a great silence. The victorious army had ridden away. The dusk had come down on all that was left of the losers.

Gibson climbed off the roof stiffly and began stumping

along the road. As he drew nearer to the battlefield, the night became full of noises again. Wounded men moaning, horses with broken knees whinnying and thrashing on the ground. Some of the women from the nearby villages had crept out with torn sheets for bandages and pails of water. They did what they could to what was left of Monmouth's army. But those left behind were beyond help. The others had been taken away as prisoners.

The dwarf traveled from one pile of slain to the next, peering anxiously into the dead mens' faces. The moon had risen now to help him. But nowhere could he find the Duke. Was that a good thing or a bad?

Nobody bothered about Richard Gibson. Elderly, grizzled and dwarfish, it was obvious that he could have played no part in the fighting. He lingered about the grief-stricken villages, hoping for news of his master. If the Duke had been taken prisoner, surely he should have heard by now!

He heard at last. It was again evening, some days later. The farmhouse which had given him shelter on the night of the battle, allowed him to stay on in return for help with the work. A party of mounted troopers stopped in the yard, demanding food and drink. They were searching that part of the countryside for hidden wounded from Monmouth's army. They first searched this house thoroughly, running their swords into every bundle of hay. Then they settled down to the meal cooked for them by the trembling woman of the house.

Gibson offered to serve it. Nothing was left now of his

fine appearance and clothes to associate him with his master the Duke. His clothes were stained and dirty, his
plumed hat lost long ago. He knew he would attract no
attention but laughter. And as he had had to endure
laughter all his life he didn't mind it now. But he thought
the conversation of the soldiers might give him the news
he longed for.

Sure enough, they laughed when he brought in the pot
of stew, and one of the men stuck his foot out idly to
watch the dwarf's contortions as he tried to avoid tripping
over it with the scalding dish in his hands.

"Bred on the farm, eh?" Another man laughed, cuffing
Gibson's ear familiarly. "Strange stock they go in for
here!"

Gibson reddened and tried to ignore the affront. It was
coarser and ruder than anything he had encountered from
the courtiers of King Charles. Presently they forgot him
and began talking among themselves. And the dwarf listened, leaning against the wall.

They were talking about the fate of the prisoners taken
after the battle of Sedgemoor. "As for the Duke," one of
them said carelessly, "they're settling his hash at the
Tower this week, so I'm told."

Gibson's knees trembled under him. He braced himself
against the wall as he asked, with a violent effort to speak
naturally, "Does your honor mean—what Duke does your
honor mean?"

"Why, the Duke of Monmouth, of course."

"He was captured then?"

"Hiding in a ditch, two days after the battle."

Another of the men, swallowing his drink, added, "Disguised as a shepherd, they say. And a pretty ticket he looked. While in his pocket was—what d'ye think?"

"Not a shepherd's crook, surely!" The men all burst out laughing.

"A handful o' peasemeal. He'd been living on that. And a medal they call the George. . . ."

They were paying no attention to the dwarf now. He might have dismissed the news as a soldier's tale but for the George. It was like his master to part with everything else but that. The insignia of the Order that had come down to him from a scaffold, to be taken from him on one. . . .

Gibson stole out of the house and started the long trudge to London. Maybe he could get there in time. Maybe his master might have some last errand for him to do. How he was to get into the Tower at all was not a problem that occupied his heavy thoughts.

It was a long way to London. By begging his food and occasionally getting a lift, the dwarf reached there only by July the fifteenth, the day fixed for Monmouth's execution. It was to take place at midday, so he heard. And the bells of the City were ringing out twelve even as he fought his way down its narrow streets through the indifferent crowds.

He was too late.

Stricken, he stood there, listening to the chimes. An old monk passing by with his rosary between his hands, stopped at the sight of the little man's contorted face, asking gently, "Are you in trouble my son?"

The last note of the last peal trembled into silence. Then Richard Gibson, born and bred a Protestant, seized the monk's robe in desperate appeal, asking, "Father, a man has just died. For God's sake, say a prayer for his soul!"

 Chapter
Sixteen

Mary was only twenty-three when her cousin Monmouth died. But she never danced again.

William, who knew that her affection for Monmouth in no way competed with her love for him, broke the news to her with unwonted gentleness. In spite of his own cold severity, he had also felt Monmouth's charm, and had even been fond of him in his own fashion.

This time Mary shed no tears at all. The shock of her father's cruel action had stunned her. She said dully, "If you had gone in his place, you would have won."

"I would never have been so foolish——" He broke off, wondering how she had meant the words. He never knew.

As before, she threw herself into her favorite pursuits to get over her grief. The new hunting-castle, Het Loo, up in Guelderland, was nearly finished now. Some of the rooms were ready for furnishing. The ladies in waiting rejoiced at the thought of moving there from the damp little rooms of the old castle. The hedges of the Maze would soon have grown high enough for them to play at getting lost in it; and the trees of the Avenue of Ceres already cast small pools of shade.

Mary's favorite spot of Het Loo was what was known as The Green Cabinet. This was an arbor outside the castle formed by vines trained over supports. Here she would sit and read her letters from Anne. The early autumns of Guelderland were still warm enough for her to do this comfortably. The leaves of the forest trees had begun to turn, but the autumn winds had not yet begun.

Anne wrote about anything and everything. The green light filtering through the vines of the arbor stained the white sheets of paper, and Anne's writing was not of the clearest anyway. But Mary loved the peace and privacy of this retreat. In it she could ponder and weigh up Anne's news.

Their father's unpopularity seemed to grow daily. It was not just a question of religion. He had no judgment, any more than Monmouth had had; but he lacked Monmouth's warmth and kindness. Anne had preserved some remnants of respect for King James longer than Mary did. But this respect was being undermined by the influence of red-haired Sarah Jennings.

Sarah had always influenced Anne. Now Sarah had been appointed Anne's Lady of the Bedchamber. She could see Anne and influence her every day. Sarah of course, was no longer Miss Jennings. She had married her Colonel Churchill. And both she and her husband were more and more disposed to back Anne's sister's chance of the throne against James's chance of retaining it.

Mary reread the last letter again thoughtfully. She was a clever woman herself, and she had learned much, since coming to Holland, of statecraft and politics from William and his able friends and advisers. How could her father do so many silly things? The latest was to command the Fellows of Magdalen College, Oxford, to choose a president who was a favorite of the King's. And when they refused his nomination (as they had every right to do), the King angrily called them "disobedient fellows" and expelled them from the college.

Where would it end? When would England's long patience be exhausted? For the people had been loyal to King James to begin with. Loyal, if not enthusiastic. As a writer of the time put it soon afterward, "King James might have kept the crown on his head as easily as his hat in a high wind."

William stepped into the arbor and stood looking down on her. Recognizing Anne's handwriting, he asked, "And what has the King of England done amiss now?"

She handed him the letter to read. He shrugged his shoulders, but said nothing. Even with her, he would make no misstep. She said after a moment or two, "Sarah

Churchill has told Anne that if things don't mend, there are those who would ask you to interfere."

He merely said one word, "How?"

She looked helplessly up at him. Had he forgotten Sedgemoor so soon? "Perhaps by remonstrating with my father."

He shook his head. "That is not what they mean. Remonstrance is useless; he would only think me impertinent to offer such a thing. No, my dear, they mean armed aid from me. I am not so foolish as to give such a thing to any one party. If the whole nation calls upon me, that's different. But the English endure patiently as a nation."

It was in the autumn of 1687 that Het Loo had first become habitable. The first snows did not come till late that year, and William lingered up here in Guelderland longer than usual, to enjoy his favorite sport. Mary wondered again how such a frail body could stand the fierce sport of boar hunting, when a man might be in the saddle for a whole day at a stretch. But the very danger of the sport seemed to give an outlet to his fiery spirit, so disciplined and controlled in ordinary life.

They went back for Christmas to The House in the Wood. Mary did not have the Orange Hall reopened at all. Perhaps she dreaded seeing a ghost dance through the other dancers; and the lights and the music would only have haunted her with the past. As it was, sometimes when walking through the woods she thought a shadow took on the shape of Monmouth and her heart would come into her mouth until the wind blew a branch apart and the shadow disappeared.

After Christmas Anne had another piece of news to impart. Their stepmother Mary Beatrice was expecting a child. She had had several, but no son had lived. England had grown used to thinking of the King's eldest daughter, Mary, being his heir. If the new baby should be a girl, Mary would still be the heir. But if the child were a boy . . .

Anne wrote that Sarah said the country would not tolerate the founding of a Catholic dynasty. As it was, they had had almost enough of James. One tiny frail straw such as a boy baby might be too much for the country's patience at last. Mary put the letter quietly aside and followed William's advice in not thinking about it any more. Her stepmother's children had always been girls, or boys who had died. This time there would only be another dead boy, or perhaps a small stepsister twenty-three years younger than herself. . . .

When that summer of 1688 came it found Mary at Honselaarsdijk. Generally the Court removed from there as soon as the tulips had blossomed. This year, for some reason or other, William preferred that they remained where they were. They were nearer to Amsterdam for one thing. And all news came to a great port like Amsterdam quicker than to the stodgy seclusion of The Hague.

In June came the news that a healthy son had been born to Mary Beatrice; a son immediately created Prince of Wales.

In July, they heard that the Presbyterians and the Anglican clergy had formed a union to oppose the King in favor of the Prince of Orange. A little later, by way of retaliation, James removed all Protestant officers from his army. And still the Prince of Orange gave no clue as to his attitude, but went about his business as usual. Once, indeed, he let fall a remark to Mary, over which she pondered when he had gone.

"If your father does not see the writing on the wall, the King of France does."

"Why, what do you mean?"

"His Catholic Majesty has offered King James thirty thousand men to defend his crown. The offer has been refused."

Mary drew a sharp breath of relief. She had no ambition to take her father's place and dreaded a future when she might have to do so. She said more cheerfully, "That means my father is confident that he needs no help."

But William only said, "He has the overconfidence of a fool."

It was a long, hot summer. Mary felt sometimes that the season would never end. She felt poised on the edge of a precipice. Anne's letters she tried to disregard. They were practically inspired by Sarah who was always a mischief-maker. Her stepmother's letters she found more difficult to forget, for she had loved Mary Beatrice. But her estrangement from her father had estranged her there, too.

She had written her congratulations on the birth of the baby, but her own straightforward nature had prevented her from sending letters as warm as she once would have

written. Feeling no jealousy for the child and no ambition
for herself, she was wise enough to know that its arrival
might well prove that last straw about which William had
spoken. So her congratulations rang hollow. How could
she write gaily and freely to someone over whom doom
was hanging?

Mary Beatrice felt the restraint in the letter. She answered pathetically to her "Dear Lemon." She wrote "You
are not so kind as you used to be. . . . You have never once
in your letters to me taken the least notice of my son, no
more than if he had never been born. . . . You have for
him the last indifference."

The last indifference. Mary sat quiet with the letter
dropped on her lap. She was searching her own mind. Was
it possible that this indifference sprang from a pang of
jealousy, caused by the fact that she herself had no son?
No. She knew it was not that. She knew she had forced her
indifference to prevent her affection going out toward a
child whom she was never likely to see.

The scorching heat of August caught the gilded balconies of the Palace. There were no woods around it to
cool the air. Yet William kept saying, "Let us wait here a
little longer." She wanted to ask, "For what?"

He dropped one of his dry hints one day. A messenger
had arrived at Honselaarsdijk; an Englishman, Mary was
told, although he came and went so quickly she never saw
him. But William told her why the messenger had come.

"He came from the Earl of Shrewsbury. The Earl has
gone the length of mortgaging his whole estate in order to

have funds for your Cause, Mary. His sword he offers to me."

"*My* cause?" She shrank from the words, saying quickly, "Does that mean there will be fighting shortly?"

William smiled and shook his head. "One sword is not of much use. And one swallow does not make a summer."

Chapter
Seventeen

So then Mary knew what William was waiting for.

He was waiting for a summons to help to depose her father. Wiser than Monmouth, he refused to take one swallow as a sign that summer had come. The Earl of Shrewsbury's sword and estate were not enough. Britain's call for help must be unanimous, or he refused to move.

It was September now. The fields were a uniform golden-brown instead of colored like a patchwork quilt. They seemed to lie waiting, too. And it was hot, unusually so for Holland, where fresh breezes generally blew in from the sea. Mary felt that an expedition down the canals might at least yield a breath of air from the water.

She knew suddenly what she would do. She would go and see Joanna Palz.

William had given her, last year, a beautiful new barge in which to make her progresses through the country. It was bigger than the old one and required two horses to tow it from the banks. She felt it would please William if she used it, although its magnificence seemed to her out of place among those quiet fields.

Once more, it was the stout Baroness's turn to be in attendance. Although the Baroness loathed the country and was not in the least interested in wasting an afternoon down a canal, Mary knew she would be deeply affronted if somebody else was chosen to take her place. Mary sighed. If only she had somebody young and gay to accompany her on such excursions! But her Court was mostly composed of members of noble families who stood on their dignity and were of a certain age.

They could not, for instance, be imagined as fitting into life in any of the London palaces. And yet . . . Mary shrank from the thought which had crossed her mind. By God's providence it might never happen that she would have to take any of them back to England in her train. . . .

The formal gardens of Honselaarsdijk made a suitable background for the new barge. Marble steps, stone urns filled with flowers, and statues of gods and goddesses led to an ornamental basin where its magnificence of gold and scarlet rocked gently on the water. The gilded dolphin at its prow already faced the unobtrusive waterway leading out of this small lake. The two white horses waited quietly, in charge of the man who would lead them. Their harness of silver and scarlet gleamed against their white coats. Mary stepped on board the barge and seated herself under the glass canopy and the gilded crown above it.

The Baroness sat down carefully on some cushions facing her mistress. It was all very well so long as the barge remained where it was, among the natural surroundings of a court. But when the horses which drew it started plodding away from civilization, her spirits went down, just as Mary's began to go up.

The velvety fields rested Mary's eyes, just as they bored the eyes of the Baroness to extinction. Here and there someone had made a bonfire of the withered stalks and debris, and the blue smoke drifted toward them; a pleasant antumnal perfume that, again, reminded the Princess of her youth at Richmond, (How long ago it all seemed!) while her lady in waiting held a lace handkerchief to her nose.

Mary had taken her favorite embroidery with her, but had dropped it on her knee to look at the landscape. She picked it up again so as to hide a look of mischief as she said, "You have never been out of Holland, I think? You don't know our fields and forests over in England! Would you like to see them someday?"

The Dutchwoman gave her a quick look, but Mary's head purposely bent over her embroidery frame. It was difficult for the Baroness to know what to say! On the one hand, everyone was talking about what was happening and what might happen in England, but Heaven forfend

that she should be expected to leave Holland and go there
to attend her Highness when she became Queen!

On the other hand, it was a great honor to attend a
queen. One must think of that.

So she only said cautiously, "It depends upon circumstances, Madam."

They seemed to have gone a long way by now. The sun
was directly overhead and its rays, deflected through the
glass canopy of the barge, made one feel quite warm. The
Baroness fanned herself. Presently, she hoped, they would
stop by a clump of willows or something that gave shade,
and the royal bargeman would set out the food from the
hamper: the jellied chicken, the fine pink ham and new
rolls and butter and fruit.

At this moment Mary said, "I am sure you must be
quite hungry, Baroness. We shall be offered something, I
know, by the couple who live in that farm and whom I
have come to see."

And, looking across the fields, the stout Dutchwoman
saw with horror that they had come back to that primitive
place were they had had such a coarse meal three or four
years ago. . . .

Mary was already stepping light-heartedly out of the
barge. A little boy came running down the field path
toward them, shouting and pointing at the gold dolphin
which rocked up and down, blazing under the sun. This
must be the baby, grown older. Grown old enough to be a
nuisance and even climb into her Highness's lap since

her Highness always made the mistake of encouraging youth. . . .

Joanna was washing clothes in a tub outside the door. She wiped the suds out of her eyes to see who it was. Then, drying her hands hastily on her apron, she took Mary's and kissed it warmly. Her husband was not at home. She led the visitors into the kitchen where, as the Baroness had anticipated, there was a large cauldron of soup to be offered them, and also a new baby lying in the cradle which had been occupied by the older one last time.

"You look just the same, Joanna. A little plumper perhaps, but then so am I. And are you still happy?"

"How can I not be, Highness? I have a good man, and those two." She indicated the children.

Inwardly Mary sighed. Not only for the happiness of children granted to Joanna but denied to her. Joanna had found her niche in the world, here among the fields of her own land. She could never be transplanted to any other country. Her place was here and not at Court, handling brushes and combs and fastening silk gowns on her mistress. . . .

It was then that Mary recognized the faint, ridiculous hope which had prompted her to visit Joanna. It was too absurd even to be uttered, and after the simple meal she left without uttering it. But she drew Joanna to her and kissed her as though they might not see each other again.

The Bargeman, seeing them coming, withdrew the stake to which the crimson ropes had been tied, and hastily threw the silver harness over the horses' backs

again. The barge glided away once more. The Baroness,
feeling sleepy (for which she blamed the heavy bean
soup), dozed on her pile of cushions. She woke up to feel
that the steady, pulling motion had ceased. They were
motionless in the shade of a row of willows.

"I took pity on the horses," the Princess was saying.
"They have plodded under the sun long enough."

Certainly it was cooler and pleasanter here. The Bargeman, having knocked the mooring pole into the ground
again with sharp blows of a hammer, now entered the
barge in his scarlet and silver livery, to serve the refresh-
ments packed in a hamper. It was the hour when the Princess liked her tea. The Baroness would have infinitely preferred a glass of wine or even beer. But the cold, strained
tea was poured out ceremoniously, and the spicy Dutch
biscuits served with it. The Baroness had no idea where
she was, and said so.

"Look to your left!" said her mistress.

There, on the horizon stood up unmistakably, the familiar tower of Utrecht. They had come a long way. Behind them, casting a grateful shade at their backs, stood
the clump of willows. The gold dolphin glared sightlessly
down a carpet of water lilies. The towpath stretched past
the willows, losing itself behind their screen of leaves. The
Baroness, looking over her shoulder, was aware of a figure
standing there, staring between the willows.

The girl, seeing she was noticed, came slowly forward.
She wore a rose-colored cotton dress and was tall and
graceful. She had seen the crown surmounting the glass

canopy, and had recognized the even taller woman sitting under it. So, when she drew level with the barge at last, she made a deep curtsey.

Mary's beautiful eyes had grown more shortsighted than ever. She saw the blur of rose, the graceful outline, the dip of the obeisance, but she could not see distinctly, so did not recognize, the girl's face. Yet something foreign, something more elegant than the movements of the country girls of the district, awoke her interest in the figure standing politely there.

She said something to her lady in waiting. The latter stuck her head out of the little window of the glass compartment and called out in Dutch, "Her Royal Highness bids you come on board!"

The barge was moored only a foot or so from the bank. The girl stepped aboard easily. As she did so, the elderly Dutchwoman vacated her place and seated herself rather grumpily outside the glass cabin which held only two.

Still Mary did not recognize her new visitor. She said in Dutch, "You are not one of my people, I think?"

As she spoke, she glanced sideways at the rose-colored dress cut low at the neck like her own, instead of being filled in; at the girl's hair, glossy and chestnut and unbound by even a snood.

"No Madam. I am from Scotland."

The Princess began to speak in English at once. "I thought when I saw you standing there, that you and I came from the same direction! In fact—" the velvet-black eyes turned again sideways trying to make out features which, now they were seen properly, grew familiar—"What is your name?"

"Grizel Hume. But here I go by the name of Grizel Wallace."

"But, of course! You must excuse me my dear, my sight is so bad that unless I see people close or am accustomed to them daily . . . You sang to me once, when the Prince and I visited your father."

"And my brother Patrick serves in his Highness' guard."

"I know." Mary nodded her head. "I've seen him, standing straight and handsome with such elegant ruffles on his wrists!"

Grizel laughed. "To tell your Highness the truth, they're the only pair he has! I wash and darn them at night when he's asleep."

"And he gives me always so gallant a bow! But the Prince has already told me something of your own story, Grizel. Tell me more. How your family came here and what you have suffered. It isn't often that I get the chance to speak and listen to my native tongue!"

Grizel hesitated. To give her confidence, Mary picked up her embroidery again, holding it close to her eyes as though absorbed in the stitches. "Well?" she said gently. "You must surely have been very young when your father, Sir Patrick met his—misfortunes. You played an active part in saving his life, I believe?"

Grizel forced herself to begin. But presently she found Mary so good and sympathetic a listener that she forgot entirely she was speaking to the wife of the Ruler of Hol-

land, herself Princess and Heiress of Great Britain and
Ireland. The beautiful, gracious woman sitting by her side
drew out Grizel's story easily by her own sympathy and
charm.

Sitting there in this fantastic float of glass and gilding,
with the flat foreign fields around her, Grizel went back in
memory to those dangerous years at home. Once more she
was a little girl of twelve, sent in to Edinburgh to visit her
father's friend imprisoned in the grim Tollbooth. Once
more she beguiled the jailers into thinking her only a
harmless child while she gave the prisoner, Robert Baillie,
the smuggled message from her father.

Once more, riding home again, she looked up at the
terrible, severed heads nailed to the city gates and knew
that her father's head might decorate it too, if she did not
manage to hide him safely. And though the late afternoon
sun still blazed down on the quiet Dutch landscape, she
thought it was moonlight again, and saw herself stealing
through the churchyard, afraid of the black shadows starting from every grave, bound for the vault in which Sir
Patrick lay hiding. . . .

"I cannot tell your Highness the relief with which we
all managed to sail to this country and live here in safety!"
she finished. Then she sighed and turned, making a little,
empty gesture with her hands. "And yet—your Highness
will forgive me when I say that I would give the whole
world to see Scotland once more!"

"Someday you shall," said the Princess gently. "Faithfulness is always rewarded in the end. Of that I am quite
convinced."

Grizel sighed again. "Highness, there are others left at home, who are equally faithful to their religion and the principles of freedom. What is going to happen to them?"

Mary said, even more gently, "You are thinking of one in particular? Some young man perhaps?"

A wave of color flushed Grizel's face. "I am thinking of—of George Baillie, the son of my father's old friend. We were trysted almost as children. He's over here now and a member of the Prince's Guard. But his estate is confiscated —he is penniless. And my parents are always urging me to marry some rich Dutchman or other!"

Mary patted her hand. "I told you I believe faithfulness is always rewarded."

The two fell silent. Here, in this ornate glass cabin Grizel felt enclosed in a dream that shut her away from the dangers and the problems of the world. She would have to wake up. But just now it was so pleasant to sit here on soft down cushions, with a beautiful princess beside one! To forget, for a moment, there were such things as death and lovers' separations. . . .

She was watching a dragonfly poised for the moment on the cup of a water lily. She was taken by surprise when Mary suddenly bent from her elegant Stuart height and kissed her softly on the cheek, saying, "Brave girl! Yet there's something you have still, which I never had. Something I truly envy."

"What can that be, Madam?" Glancing up, astonished, Grizel saw that the black eyes above her were glistening with tears.

The Princess answered slowly, "You have a father

whom you can love and respect. I was taken away from mine when I was but a child. I was brought up by strangers. Nobody gave me the opportunity to show faithfulness. Or love."

Grizel did not know what to answer, so she remained silent. The Princess picked up her embroidery again quickly, as if she regretted uttering her words. There followed another long silence. Suddenly they both saw the Baroness, who sat so grumpily in the prow by the golden dolphin, turn her head, as though listening.

The next moment they both heard it, too. The sound of a horse galloping hard down the towpath toward them, as if its rider had some fierce purpose in making speed.

The rider came into view the next moment. He was one of the officers of William's guard. Mary half rose, putting her head out of the little window in the glass cabin and calling, "What is the matter? Have you a message for me?"

The officer had dismounted. Now he sprang onto the barge which dipped and rocked under his weight. He pulled out a letter and handed it to Mary. "The Prince sends you this, Highness. It is urgent. He asks you to return to him immediately."

The Baroness's large mouth had fallen open. Now she watched her mistress read the letter and noticed how pale Mary suddenly became. She was leaning against her cushions now, as if she felt faint.

Grizel Hume looked at her in alarm. "Is—is it bad news, Madam?"

Mary forced herself to open her eyes to speak. "Yes—no.

Never mind child, you will hear it shortly yourself. Then
it will be good or bad, as others make it. You must go
now." She kissed Grizel once more. "Farewell. But I think
we shall meet again."

The officer had shouted an order to the Bargeman, who
came running from his place under one of the willows.
The horses were yoked to the red towropes again and the
mooring stake taken hurriedly out of the ground. Grizel
had gained the towpath again. She stood there, watching
while the glorious floating coach disappeared round a
bend of the canal, and the carpet of water lilies, which had
submerged at its approach, now slowly appeared and spread
itself out again.

She wondered what the news could be that everyone was
soon to know.

Meanwhile the barge threaded the waterways until it
reached the hidden entry to the gardens of Honselaarsdijk.
Here a more formal canal, lined with clipped hedges and
statues, took the magnificent vessel into the lake or basin
lying before the palace. Hardly was it moored when Mary,
not waiting to be assisted, jumped from it and went
quickly up the marble steps leading to the terrace.

They told her William was in his writing cabinet. She
burst into the room and stood there a moment unable to
speak for want of breath. Still gasping from the hurried
climb, she fixed her eyes on his face, asking her question
with them, imploringly.

"Yes, it is true." He told her. "They have sent for me at
last."

She dropped onto a nearby chair and laying her head on its arm burst into tears.

He was saying, "I am deeply sorry for this, Mary. If I can still avoid a direct battle with your father—if only he has the sense to abdicate . . ."

She raised her head, staring at him wildly. "You can refuse to go!"

He shook his head. "The British want me to restore their liberties. It is my duty to go."

 Chapter
Eighteen

Never had Richard Gibson remembered an English autumn so long and so cold.

Hunger makes one feel the cold. And one monotonous day after another, spent in hiding, makes time stretch to eternity. In this great ant heap of London, maybe the dwarf might have gone about freely unnoticed. Certainly few would have recognized, in the shabby, bent figure with the stained clothes, the swaggering buffoon of King Charles's court.

But somebody might. After all, he was a dwarf and as such an object of curiosity. And he had served Monmouth long enough for folk to associate him with the man executed as a traitor. There was a dealer in secondhand clothes, who used to be glad enough to buy his fine suits for children to dress up in. John Jemson, his name was. An ardent Protestant, a bigoted man to whom the very word "Catholic" acted like poison.

John Jemson took him in.

The dwarf was too frightened of being recognized, to offer himself anywhere for work. And he was too proud to eat more than one meal a day at Jemson's table. He would slip out of the house early, to hide himself in the most crowded sections of the city and try to pick up intelligence of what was happening—or going to happen. And at night he pretended he had had an invitation to supper.

So he had, in a way. There was a wineshop near Wapping Stairs, down by the river. Its owner was an old crony of his. He, too, had come from Cumberland long ago. In his days of splendor at court, Gibson had grown ashamed of knowing the man. Now he was grateful for the evening's warmth and the glass of ale which, with a piece of bread, made his supper. Even so, his pride made him insist upon paying for this by taking a turn at filling the tankards and cleaning them afterward.

It was a poor little place enough. So when the sergeant clanked in with two of his cronies, they gave it quite an air. At sight of their uniforms Gibson had vanished into the back room where the dishes were washed up. But the sergeant had caught sight of him and wanted some sport.

"Hey, landlord! Is that Robin Goodfellow you have to do your work for you? Let's have a look at him!"

So Gibson had had to come forward, and stand being the butt of their jokes which he didn't mind as he saw they had no interest in him except as a joke. Afterward they stood him drinks, and the little man whose head was weakened by hunger, grew very merry, though not sufficiently so to give himself away; unless it was when he boasted about having lived in Holland.

By this time they were all singing. And Gibson, to gain prestige, told them proudly he knew some of the songs the Dutch troops sang in camp. To prove his words, he gave them "Lillibulero." The tune was catchy and the soldiers learned it at once. When the time came to pay their reckoning and go, they stumbled out into the night, shouting "Lilli-Lilli-Lillibulero!" just as if they belonged to the Dutch army themselves.

And one of them, the one with the best ear for carrying a tune, was to take his turn on guard at St. James's Palace not so very long after.

As September gave way to October, the dwarf could feel the popular mood hardening against King James. So did the King himself. By October he was forced by public opinion to restore the rights he had taken from the Oxford College, and to put Protestant magistrates back in their places. But by now it was all too late.

On October 15, the Prince of Wales was baptized. There was no enthusiasm and no crowds. Yet still, Parliament held its hand and the people remained patient, all but a party of influential men who had already been in touch with William of Orange.

Gibson did not know that. He only knew that when winter came he would be colder and hungrier than ever. He cursed the easygoing patience of the English, and he still refused to sponge on Jemson. The night of the baby's christening, he ventured to go into the courtyard of St. James's Palace, knowing there would be much coming and going and fine carriages letting down guests for the banquet that evening. It would also be dark. Even though this was his old haunt, the torchlight would be too dazzling for people to see him clearly. And there was always the odd coin to be picked up in return for holding the heads of restive horses. . . .

It gave him a strange feeling to be here again. To see the court carriages set down their occupants under the porte-cochere where he had many a time seen King Charles himself dismount. There, too, was the little window where the girls, Mary and Anne and Sarah, used to stand looking . . .

And there, by Jupiter, was one of them—Sarah herself!

She had descended from her coach and was waiting for her husband to join her before entering the Palace. He might not have known her, she had grown so tall and fine. But he heard her name called; and now that the torchlight shone on her hair, he recognized its blazing red tint and the haughty carriage of her head.

After all, he had been acquainted with her from childhood. He had even taught her drawing. So, made bold by that, he stole up to her and tugged her sleeve.

She drew away angrily. One hand went up as though

it would box his ears. But he said quickly, "Don't you remember me, my Lady? I remember you when you were nawt but Sarah Jennings."

She bent down and stared at him. Then she exclaimed, "Gibson the Dwarf?"

"Aye." He nodded his head. "I'm not so fine as I used to be. But I take no alms from anyone nor ask none. I don't call it alms to ask you the price of a meal. I've saved ye trouble often enough!"

"Poor Mr. Gibson! How did you fall on such evil days!" An unwonted look of sympathy came into her face. Probably he reminded her of the carefree days of her childhood. Her hand plunged into the silk purse hanging by a gold chain to her side. Suddenly her expression hardened. "Oh, I remember . . ."

He had heard the coins chinking as her fingers groped among them. His eyes glistened already at the thought of tasting meat, or maybe even a bit of game pie if Sarah was generous enough.

"I remember now." She repeated slowly. "Were you not with the Duke of Monmouth over in Holland? Then you must have returned with him when he came to head the Rebellion against the King . . ."

He might have assured her he had taken no part in the fighting. But pride and contempt kept him quiet. She withdrew her hand from the purse, empty, saying, "I am sorry, I cannot help you."

And she turned away from him and entered the Palace on her husband's arm.

He spat after her. No so much because now he must do without supper, as with scorn at her waiting to see which way the cat would jump. If the Prince of Orange's invasion came to nothing, she and her husband would still stand well with King James. Meanwhile she would not risk a penny piece in helping a known associate of the King's chief enemy, Monmouth.

Hunger hit him again like a blow. It was humiliating, but it was true. There was someone else, though, from whom he would not mind asking the price of his supper. Aye, and she would be kind too! He could not imagine her treating him as Sarah had a few minutes before. His eyes peered through the darkness striving eagerly to make out the liveries of each carriage as it drove up.

"Has not the Princess Anne arrived yet?" he asked the man standing beside him.

The other stared down at him in surprise. "I see you're a countryman by your speech or you would know she's far enough off."

"She would be here for her stepbrother's christening, surely!"

"I told ye, she's left London. Off to Denmark with her Danish husband to be out of trouble."

"Trouble?" His heart sank.

The fellow gave him a good-humoured nudge. "We'd all do the same if we knew what was good for us. They say the Dutch are going to try to invade us again."

Gibson slipped away. Presently he reached the wine-shop at Wapping Stairs. Although his supper was only the

usual crust of bread and drink of ale, his hunger seemed
suddenly assuaged by hope. If the Prince of Orange did
come, then with him would come the dwarf's old mistress,
the Princess Mary. She would not see him starve!

The torchlight died down in St. James's Courtyard. The
music and dancing stopped. And presently another cold,
autumn day stole across the Park, blowing against the
palace windows with its damp breath. It was the eleventh
hour for King James. Now was the time when he should
have been counting his supporters. Instead, his belief in
the divine right of kings, coupled by his stupidity, kept
him from doing anything at all.

Mary Beatrice, mother of the newborn baby, had more
sense. She listened to the stories of how William was gathering an army together, and she grew cold with fear for
her son. She refused to believe that Mary, whom she had
once loved and called her Dear Lemon, could possibly
approve or let William do such a thing.

She wrote a frenzied letter to her saying, "I never will
believe that you are to come over with him; for I know
you to be too good, that I don't believe that you could
have such a thought against the worst of fathers, much less
perform it against the best."

When Mary got the letter, she only sighed and put it
aside. Then, like the rest of the world, like London itself,
she waited to see what would happen next.

At St. James's, the King was busy giving sittings to Mr.
Kneller who was painting his portrait. It was a soothing,
gratifying occupation to assist in the making of a master-

piece. Besides, the picture must be finished; he had promised to give it to his good friend Mr. Pepys. So, handsome,
melancholy, obstinate, he sat there with his best suit on,
while those who attended his Court grew fewer every day,
and all sorts of rumors flooded the City. . . .

Autumn was approaching early that year. Perhaps the
damp, heavy air, the dead leaves blowing against the windows, the frightened face of Mary Beatrice, did have their
effect in the end. He began to believe, though with difficulty, that his people were planning to get rid of him.
That his own daughter should help them, passed his com-
prehension. He took time off from the sittings, to write
her a letter of dignified inquiry and reproof.

He began by telling her that he had heard of her husband's plans for invading England. He went on, "I hope it
will be as great a surprise to you as it was to me when I
first heard it, being sure it is not in your nature to approve
so unjust an undertaking." And he finished, rather sadly,
"I shall say no more but that I shall always have as much
kindness for you as you will give me leave to have."

The letter took time and many hazards before it
reached Mary. By then, the picture was finished. By then
too the King's full apprehensions must have been roused
at last. But if London was preparing itself to turn against
him, there was always his faithful Catholic Kingdom, Ireland. Perhaps Mary Beatrice's tears, her fear for her son, at
last overcame him. But there is another, more pic-
turesque, story.

Lying sleepless in the dark, King James could hear the

footfalls of the sentry pacing the courtyard down below. On this night, the man was one of the company who had passed the time singing with Gibson at the wineshop on Wapping Stairs.

Now, to pass the time again, he whistled softly as he marched to and fro under the King's window. He whistled the tune the dwarf had taught him. It had not spread yet to England, but James knew it. He knew it was a favorite air of William's Dutch troops. William was famed for moving his troops quickly and secretly. It would not be the first time that a Dutch fleet had sailed right up the Thames.

"Lilli—Lilli—Lillibulero!"

By next morning, the King and his family had fled.

 Chapter
Nineteen

When Mary received her father's letter, she sat still a long while after reading it.

It cut her to the heart. He meant that it should. But years ago, he had handed her over to a stranger whom she had feared and loathed. He had refused to listen to her pleadings. He had ordered her to obey her new husband.

Well, she had learned to love William. It was her duty to obey him, too.

Yet the letter showed her something else which she could, and ought, to do. With it in her hand, she went straight to William. He was poring over a military map and looked up with slight annoyance at being interrupted. But when he saw how upset she was, he took the letter she held out to him and read it in silence.

She said, "I have one thing to ask of you. To demand of you."

Astonished at her unusual firmness, he asked what it was.

"If my father should ever become your prisoner," she replied, "you must promise me not to serve him as he served Monmouth."

Must! It was a word she had never used to him before, nor had he ever heard those tones before. Standing there, drawn up to her full height, she looked as though she were Queen of England already. Strangely, he did not feel angry with her. He had never admired her so much.

"I promise you," he said quietly, handing the letter back.

It was October now. The roses hung half-withered on their stems, nipped by the night frosts. Mary knew that she must stay behind in Holland until William's battles were fought and won. The thought was torture to her. By day she was as confident in his success as though failure were out of the question. But in the sleepless dark she thought of Monmouth's failure and death, and she trembled with fear.

Perhaps William guessed this. Perhaps he wanted to take her thoughts away from the far future to the near one. Because during one of his hurried visits to her, he said, "My dear, it is not too early for you to be planning

your new Court in London. Think who you would like to
serve you—who you will bring over with you when you
follow me there."

She said with a trace of bitterness, "When will that be?"

He picked up the long, fashionable curl resting on her
shoulder and put it to his lips. "Believe me, the first moment possible."

They had moved to The House in the Wood. It was
nearer to The Hague and William could pay her brief
visits, as he was doing now. When he was not there, she
tried to fill in the time by selecting her finest china to go
with her to England. It seemed to make William's success
more certain, somehow. But her chief lady in waiting, the
stout Baroness, watched her with dismay.

Her mistress saw the expression. The whole of Holland
knew by now what was in the wind; the Court had been
discussing it for weeks. Mary said, "Perhaps my porcelain
will make you feel more at home when you see it in London, Baroness?"

"Perhaps, Madam," answered the other glumly.

Her mistress felt a sudden sensation of relief. Only now
did she realize how the older, stodgier members of the
Court had weighed on her spirits. Hopefully she said, "I
would not force anyone to endure London's fogs if they
preferred not to accompany me. London is—very foggy."

The Baroness seized her hand and kissed it. "What a
relief, your Highness! I wouldn't cross that nasty sea for
the highest appointment in England! I had thought my-

self able to face it, but they tell me the coffee there is made out of dregs."

Mary, too, felt greatly relieved and quite fond of the Baroness for not insisting on going with her. In any case, she would have to appoint some English noblewoman in her place. But could there not be, perhaps, somebody young and gay to wait on her—someone who did not crush her by disapproval when she wanted to enjoy herself?

She thought suddenly of Grizel Hume.

The canal in front of "Doctor Wallace's" house in Utrecht had a skin of ice now, each morning. Reluctantly Grizel had lit the stove in the tiny sitting room, because it was too cold for her parents to sit there without it. She had tried her best to save fuel during the summer and she herself would have done without for a little longer. But her mother needed the warmth.

She had the iron door of the stove open and was blowing on the sticks, when suddenly her brother Patrick walked into the room. Even in the moment of jumping to her feet to greet him, she thought how handsome he was! The uniform of the Royal Guards set him off splendidly, and you would never guess that the ruffles at his wrists were darned.

"Patrick! I thought you were on guard duty this week!"

"So I am. But I was ordered here with a special message for you. Guess who from?"

"A special message for me?" She looked at him, bewildered.

"The Princess went out to her coach while I was on

guard this morning. She recognized me, which is good news to begin with, and very gracious on her part. Grizel, that time you met her again and were asked on board her barge—she must have taken a fancy to you surely!"

"The message, Patrick!"

To tease her, he sauntered over to the little iron stove and put his hands on the metal as though concerned about its being lit properly. "You must get one of those Dutchwomen to teach you how to keep the thing stoked. There must be a free current of air——"

"*Patrick!*"

"All right. Her Highness wishes to see you tomorrow, at noon, at The House in the Wood."

It was only another of the extraordinary things that seemed to be happening lately. Patrick had looked into the kitchen first, where Lady Hume was trying to mix a pudding in rather an inexpert manner and Sir Patrick, who had a touch of ague, was sitting close to the great brick oven.

"They are saying King James has gone over to Ireland!" he cried.

His father said, "Be more explicit. Who says it?"

"It's the common gossip at Court——"

The old man got up wearily. "Hope deferred maketh the heart sick. . . . I never listen to gossip."

"Father! Ye ken the Dutch fleet is being recommissioned at this minute, and stores bought and recruits made——" In his eagerness the boy relapsed into the broad Scots he had spoken at home.

His mother suddenly cried out, "Don't raise our hopes, Patrick! It is cruel."

His spirits dashed, Patrick said rather sulkily, "Well, another English courier arrived at the Palace last night. Maybe King James hasn't gone to Ireland after all. But it's sure that Parliament's invited the Prince of Orange over to send him to——"

"Hush, my boy. And how is it you are off duty?"

"Oh, I almost forgot, and it's important. A message for Grizel . . ."

He stepped into the next room and gave it.

Grizel's mother and sisters instantly began discussing what she should wear to go to the palace. Grizel herself knew. "I'll wear the pink gown the Princess saw me in. Maybe she remembered me by it."

"But it's cotton, and the weather has turned cold."

"Lend me your good cloak then, Mother. I'll be fine and warm in it."

The cloak was a remnant of better days, brought from Scotland. It had a lining of sable and silver clasps. Grizel held its magnificence round her as she entered the palace in spite of the warmth of the stoves, which almost made her gasp. But she was reluctant to hand it to the footman who had offered to take it from her, and to enter the royal presence in only her cotton frock.

She was led through one folding door after the next. At the opening of the last door, a pack of small, silky dogs ran out yapping, and Mary's voice was heard, trying to calm them. The dogs hesitated, looked suspiciously at Grizel, then trooped back toward that soft, commanding voice.

Grizel stepped into the room which seemed like the soft heart of a rose because it was hung round entirely with curtains of rose brocade. Mary sat by the window, where an autumn leaf had already plastered itself on the sill. She had a book in her lap.

Grizel curtseyed very low, then stood still.

The Princess said with her charming smile, "I am glad to see you once more. Come, sit by me on the window seat while we talk. My stupid eyes prevent me from seeing people till they come close."

Grizel seated herself beside Mary. The perfume from Mary's silken skirts reached her as the rich folds spread themselves across the seat. The door opened silently, to let in a servant who placed a silver tray with delicate, handleless porcelain cups before them.

Mary put one of the little eggshell cups into Grizel's hand, saying, "This is the new dish, tea. Do you like it?"

Grizel sipped. The drink seemed to her bitter and strange. She said, "I had heard of it, Madam, but never tasted it. It is too expensive for us."

"Our Dutch traders bring it here from the East. I send presents of it to my sister, the Princess Anne. She is enchanted by its flavor."

Mary set down her cup. She looked directly at Grizel. "You have heard the news from England?"

Grizel answered cautiously, "Yes, if your Highness means that King James has a son."

"I mean more. My father has left London. Parliament

chooses to take this as abdication on his part, and the Prince and I have been invited to go to England. When I go, will you come with me?"

"I?" Grizel put her own little cup down hurriedly. Her fingers had begun to tremble.

"I am making up my Household. I must find out which ladies are willing to come to London with me and join our new Court. You have been faithful and loyal to both your father and your country. I know you would be equally faithful and loyal to me."

"It—it is a great honor!"

The Princess leaned forward and took Grizel's face between her two hands. "I am so shortsighted; I must see what you really think."

The large black eyes searched Grizel's face; then the hands were withdrawn. The Princess leaned back. She said disappointedly, "I see no pleasure in your countenance. What makes you hesitate?"

"Your Highness did say London?"

"Of course."

Desperately Grizel tried to find words polite enough to give a refusal without offense. She was glad to be interrupted by the folding doors opening once more. A short, frail-looking man walked softly into the room. He had fine eyes and would have been handsome, but for his nose which was large and hooked like a parrot's.

The man said, "Is this Sir Patrick Hume's daughter?"

Grizel recognized the Prince of Orange himself. She jumped up hastily and curtseyed. He gave a little bow in

return, then spoke again in his quick, abrupt way, and
with the heavy Dutch accent he never lost.

"I have always admired Sir Patrick's courage in defense
of liberty of conscience. I know he has suffered much. If
things in England go as we hope, he won't find me un-
grateful."

To Grizel this meant only one thing. "Oh Sir!" she
exclaimed. "Does that mean ye'll give us back our home in
Scotland?"

The Prince smiled. It softened his face wonderfully.
"Don't you say in Scotland that bridges mustn't be crossed
till one reaches them? Aye, and sometimes they must be
built first! But I have your father's name down for high
honor and the restoration of his estates."

Mary looked past Grizel toward her husband. She gave a
mock sigh. "Now you have lost me my new lady in waiting!"

"What's that, my dear? How can that be!"

"When I offered Miss Hume the post, she at once inquired if it meant living in London. I think her heart is in
Scotland. But if everyone's estates are to be restored, then I
believe it is not her father's home that she hopes to occupy
there!"

They were both looking at her now. She felt her cheeks
flaming. Mary began talking to the Prince, to cover the
girl's embarrassment.

"The young man favored by Miss Hume belongs to
your Guard. He has no means to marry at present. His
father gave his life for the Covenanting cause and the fam-

ily estate was forfeited. Is that not so?"

She turned to Grizel, who had such a lump in her throat she could only nod.

Then William made one of his rare gestures. He took Grizel's hand with a kindly expression, saying, "Young lady, if that is so and if I have the power to do it, I shall restore to your lover everything he has lost. Then, if you still prefer Scotland to London . . ."

His gray eyes were twinkling. Gratitude and relief swept away all her nervousness in an instant. "A thousand thanks, your Highness!" she burst out fervently. "If ever you come to England to reign, you won't find any more loyal subjects than George and me!"

Chapter
Twenty

Still William went on calmly and unhurriedly with his preparations.

He had to inform his own government of his intentions. This he did in a speech to the States-General. For once, he spoke so movingly that the stolid Dutchmen, unaccustomed to showing emotion, listened to him with the tears running down their cheeks.

They knew he might be addressing them for the last time. "If I lose my life in this expedition," the Prince told them, "take the Princess, who loves your country as she does her own, under your protection. Mind me in your public and private prayers, and I shall do the same for you."

Then he returned to Mary and spoke to her in a way she, too, had never heard from him before. She had kept a Diary from which she wrote her Memoirs long after, and their very words have come down to us still warm with emotion like living things.

"If it should be God's will that we do not meet again . . ." For a moment he could not go on. Then, forcing himself to utter the words he finished, "If that should be so, it will be necessary for you to marry again."

His words so wounded her, she too was struck dumb. Then she burst out indignantly, "I have never loved any man but you, and I should never know how to love another." At that, the cold, formal man who had never before been able to express his feelings, even to the wife whom he loved, broke down entirely. It was he who wept now, and in broken words ". . . showed me all the tenderness that I could have desired—so much indeed, that all my life I shall never forget it."

The next day they parted. It was the end of October, 1688. Autumn had already given place to winter. The preparations for sailing had taken longer than they should, and there was now the danger of winter gales. William's great fleet, crammed with men and horses, already filled the small harbor outside the village of Helvoetsluis. Other, smaller ships had joined the fleet, intending to sail under its protection. They had been chartered by the exiles from Britain who hoped to return with a victorious Prince.

The exiles poured in to Helvoetsluis on horseback, on

carts or trudging, wheeling their goods in barrows. Sir
Patrick Hume and his family were aboard a small ship
already. Lady Hume, sat, majestic, on deck, on top of a
feather mattress. Grizel, Patrick, and George Baillie had
gone ashore to seek news of when the fleet would sail.

"They await the Prince," Patrick reported on his return. His father looked anxious.

"This delay is dangerous," he said. "There's a storm
blowing up. The Prince will be well advised when he
comes to wait until it is over."

But, cautious in other ways, it was not William's habit
to wait. At dusk that evening he appeared, glimpsed
briefly as he stepped aboard his yacht and was rowed out
to the flagship moving up and down grandly in the swell.
Then it was dark. And the wind blew and the water began
to rage and boil against the sides of the harbor. The storm
drove in from the sea. It whipped roofs off and broke the
arms of the windmills on the dunes. And everyone's nostrils were full of sand.

The captain of the Humes' boat stayed all night an-
chored in the lee of the shore as did all the smaller boats.
Farther out, where the great ships lay, it was impossible to
see what was happening. The night was murky and there
was no moon. But when dawn broke, everyone rushed on
deck and looked toward the horizon.

It was empty. The Dutch navy had sailed.

"Right into the teeth o' the storm!" exclaimed the
Scotch captain, adding, "The Prince was a bold man. I doubt
he'll no' find a crown at the bottom o' the ocean."

All night while the storm raged Mary had lain awake listening to it. The wind crept into the great room and ran up and down the silken curtains enclosing her bed, and she grew icy cold as she listened. Surely William would never have put out to sea in a storm like this!

As soon as it was light enough she got up and dressed and ordered a carriage to drive her to Helvoetsluis. "Faster! Faster!" she kept ordering the coachman in a voice made harsh by anxiety. When they got within sight of the port she told him to leave the road and drive over the dunes to reach the sea border. She must catch a glimpse of the harbor as quickly as possible. . . .

The wind still battered the coast and the long grasses rippled like waves over the sand hills. The wind stung her face when she left the carriage to peer toward the water. She could see the harbor now. A few little ships, fishing boats and such, remained tied up safely in the shelter of the Mole. But of William's great navy there was no sign.

"What is this?" An object came sliding toward her on the crest of a wave. It was left at her feet on the shingle. A sailors' hammock such as was slung from the timbers of a man-o'-war. Its rope was frayed and wrenched.

"And this?"

The sea was bringing strange fruit into the harbor. Stores from William's ships, boots, seamen's chests; the people of Helvoetsluis were busy salvaging the wreckage when Mary finally reached the town and drove down to the little harbor. They were dragging a dead horse ashore.

One of the troop of cavalry horses especially embarked for the mounted regiments. . . .

"Eh Madam, dinna despair!" She started at the sound of the familiar Scots accent. The captain of the Humes' boat had come ashore. He was looking at her white face sympathetically. "This may only mean that his Highness has had to order his ships to be lightened."

"God knows!" She turned away from him and drove back to her palace again.

All through that day bits of flotsam and jetsam were brought ashore by the tide, and the bodies of five hundred cavalry horses. With no modern means of sending news, and no other boats coming through the storm into harbor, they could not tell if the grand Dutch fleet had gone to the bottom or not.

The storm had died down, but still the little ships waited, for now they dared not land in Britain without the protection of the Prince's army. For Mary, the waiting was agony. She could not stay indoors. She wandered about the withered gardens of Honselaarsdijk where a cold wind still blew and the dead leaves lay on the surface of the little lake. She walked so quickly up and down the terraces, her lady in waiting could scarcely reach her side with offers of cloaks and furs which were impatiently waved aside.

At last a horseman, galloping hard all the way from Helvoetsluis, reached the palace with news. A four-masted brig had just reached the harbor, greatly battered by the storm. But it brought word that the Dutch fleet was safe. It had been forced to anchor and ride out the storm after lightening the ships by throwing everything overboard that could be thrown.

Immediately all the little boats that had been cowering for shelter inside the harbor, sailed out like chickens seeking their mother's wings. It was calm now, with the exhausted stillness that falls on the air after violent disturbance. Once more Mary had to wait at home. Wait day after day. . . .

Until she got word that William had landed safely at Torbay, on the coast of Devon, on the fifth of November, 1688.

His invading troops were reinforced by wholesale desertions from the King's army. King James had marched the troops to Salisbury and then, fearing a battle, had returned to London. There, there was no enthusiasm for his Cause. At last facing the truth, James finally fled with his wife and baby son to France.

There was no royal standard over the palace now. Richard Gibson, drawn back to it by old memories as well as by curiosity, hung about the courtyard day after day along with the crowd of idlers who did the same. No sentries marched up and down keeping guard. The whole city was like an apple with its core withdrawn.

Now that the winter had really come, the chestnut roaster who had his stand at the corner of St. James's Street, boldly moved it into the courtyard itself. His brazier cast a little pool of warmth around it, and into that pool were sucked the idle who felt the cold most, or who had the price of a few hot chestnuts in their pockets.

Gibson had made some pence by sweeping a street for a fine lady. He stood by the brazier, tossing the delicious roast chestnuts from one hand to another to cool them and to thaw his fingers at the same time. Having long since lost his plumed hat, he had scavenged an old felt one and, with the last echo of his former flourish, had stuck a pheasant's feather in its greasy hatband. Mr. Jemson had given him a coat far too large, so that it flapped ludicrously about his ankles. He would have made a figure of fun to the by-standers had they not grown accustomed to seeing him there.

As it was, they ignored him, talking over his head. "Him reign over us?" one of the men was saying con-temptuously. "No Dutch foreigner'll do that! No, 'tis the Lady Mary who is the heir. And a different queen she'll make from Bloody Mary, thank the Lord!"

"Ah, but a woman can't reign proper!"

Another man put in, "And what about her husband doing all the work o' sending King James packing? Is he to get no reward for that?"

The dwarf listened, peeling his chestnuts and cramming them into his mouth. Whether the Prince or the Princess of Orange was sovereign, he knew that his place would soon be restored to him. He had only to enter the palace and say who he was. . . . Momentarily, he forgot his ap-pearance and the difficulty of getting through the palace guards, dressed as he was now and looking as he did.

He saw the days of hunger receding from him al-ready.

Suddenly a wing of the palace seemed to be springing to life. A servant passed from one window to the next, dragging the curtains apart to let in the winter light. And from one or two of the chimney stacks a trickle of brown smoke began to reach up to the sky from newly lit fires.

It was still early enough. A carriage entered the courtyard and set down a man whom the crowd instantly recognized. My Lord Shrewsbury. What was he doing here? Another carriage rolled in, and another. The men they brought were leading representatives of the Houses of Parliament, and well known to a London crowd. Something obviously was going to happen.

Yet the chief newcomer slipped across the courtyard on foot so quietly the little knot of onlookers scarcely noticed him until he had vanished under the hood of the portecochere. They burst out laughing when the dwarf swept off his shabby hat and made a low bow toward the retreating back of the short, slim man who had just arrived.

"Who is it you've done obeisance to?" asked one of them with a wink toward the others.

"That was the Prince of Orange." Gibson added with dignity, "I was well acquainted with him in Holland."

They burst out laughing again at this flight of fancy. Upstairs, one of the dusty rooms of the old palace had been prepared for a Council of State. William's friend Count Bentinck had slipped into the palace as unobtrusively as the other. They had begun their debate before the Prince's arrival, and Bentinck had sat, angry and sullen, while the English lords discussed what was to be done with his master once Mary was firmly set on the throne.

At last he could remain silent no longer. "If you want my private opinion," he broke in, "the Prince of Orange won't agree to being only his wife's gentleman usher!"

Danby, one of the statesmen who had urged William to come over, said coldly, "I have already written to her Highness on that point."

"What did you say?"

"That we have no doubt but that we shall be able to set her alone on the throne."

"Alone on the throne!" Bentinck's exclamation was interrupted by the Prince's entry. William's face betrayed his weariness. He had suffered from asthma the night before and had in any case traveled fast and long to reach London at all. But he held himself taut as ever. Giving a cold nod to the men around him, he asked them curtly what they were there to offer.

There was a hemming and hawing around the table. Presently someone bolder than the others mentioned the country's gratitude to him, and the position they were willing to cede him as consort to the reigning Sovereign. "This we have already written to the Lady Mary," he added.

The speaker was taken aback when William said calmly, "I know. Her answer will be in your hands presently. But she sent a copy of it to me, by swift messenger, and as you may want to know her decision as soon as possible, I shall read you what she says now."

He drew a paper from his pocket and read, "I am the

Prince's wife and would never be any other than in conjunction with him."

The men, startled, looked at one another wondering how to take this new development. Only Bentinck appeared delighted. William was speaking again in his dry, crisp tones. Their amazed ears heard him say that he would be content with what he called a "conjunctive sovereignty" and that only if he had sole administration of the country.

"I think it proper to let you know," he was saying, "I will accept no dignity dependent on the life of another. I will not oppose the Princess' rights; I respect her virtues; no one knows them better than I do. Crowns to others may have charms, but I think it proper also to let you know that I will hold no power dependent on the will of a woman. Therefore, if these schemes are adopted, I can give you no assistance in the settlement of the nation, but will return to my own country."

There was a moment of thunderstruck silence. William rose and beckoned to Bentinck to follow him into the next room, leaving the Englishmen to make up their minds. They conversed almost in whispers at first. They had thought to find a puppet in the Prince of Orange, and to be able to manage his wife even while crowning her queen.

But the Prince had spoken with a sharp decisiveness which showed them he meant what he said.

Finally, Lord Halifax was chosen to give William their decision. This he did in the offhand English manner which, to the day of his death, William detested.

Opening the door of the inner room, Lord Halifax's actual words were: "You may be what you please. As nobody knows what to do with you, so nobody knows what to do without you."

 Chapter
Twenty-one

William would not allow his wife to join him until everything was once more in order in England. He wanted to be sure that she would be welcomed as Queen. So Mary had three months to look her last on the country she had come to as a girl of fifteen and had grown to love.

She looked for the last time on the flat Dutch landscape sparkling under its winter snow. She skated for the last time down the canals, wondering whether the lake in St. James's Park would have ice deep enough to bear her. She said farewell, with regret, to the comfortable warmth of the stoves, remembering the smoke and the scorching of the great fires in her uncle's palace, where the heat never reached the corners of the rooms.

She turned her silver taps on and off meditatively, de-
termining that this, at least, could be copied. She would
have a bathroom with running water, in whatever palace
it suited William to live in best.

She thought that would probably be Hampton Court.
Her William needed good country air for his asthma. She
tried to still her loneliness and fear of this new step by
planning in her mind's eye just where her collection of
Eastern porcelain would look best. It had been carefully
packed and crated many weeks past.

Now that she was leaving them, the Dutch nation
grieved at her going. Their Prince they knew they would
see again. During his absence in England, they could be
ruled by the States-General, and it was likely that he
would return more than once, either to fight for them or
to make sure they were governed properly.

But Mary they would never see again. She was going
back to her own country to reign over it. Women do not
move about or make wars.

She landed at Margate on February 10, 1689. Two days
later she reached London and entered St. James's where
William was waiting for her. At first her joy at seeing him
again blotted out her feelings at being in her uncle's old
palace once more. When she had embraced him and clung
to him, he disengaged her gently, saying, "There are some
old friends waiting to greet you in the Long Corridor."

Anne and her husband she had already met when she
disembarked. Anne had grown very fat, she was sorry to
notice. She must really speak to her about eating so much

spun sugar and sweetmeats. . . . But then she looked at
Anne's husband, Prince George, and saw he was even fat-
ter. Perhaps after all, one could scarcely rebuke a wife for
the tastes she evidently shared with her husband. . . .

They had driven on ahead of her, and were standing in
the Long Corridor to greet her. So was Sarah Churchill
with her husband, later to become the Duke of Marlborough and the ancestor of another great Englishman,
Winston Churchill, born many generations later. Everyone dipped low curtseys or bows. Tired as Mary was, and
longing to be alone with William, her natural charm and
graciousness warmed them all. Her manners atoned for
William's whose cold abruptness, understood by the
Dutch, repelled the English.

Yet he could be kindly too. For now he was dragging
forward an odd little figure tricked out at last in a decent
set of clothes.

"Here is an old friend whom you will be glad to see!"

"Mr. Gibson!" Mary's face flushed with pleasure, for the
dwarf was almost the only remaining part of her old life as
a girl.

Sarah, who happened to be standing next to them, said
sweetly, "Indeed, your Majesty, neither you nor I would
be able to draw a straight line but for Mr. Gibson's former
services!" And Mary was a little puzzled to see a sudden
look of rage, instead of gratitude for the compliment, pass
over the dwarf's features.

There, in a corner of one of the State Rooms, Mary
came on the portrait of her father, left abandoned on its

easel. The melancholy, handsome face looked at her with such reproach that she burst into tears. William must have noticed it, too, and her distress, for next day it was gone.

The following month King James landed in Ireland from France. He meant to make one last bid for the throne for himself and his baby son, and it was likelier to find help with his Irish Catholic subjects than his English Protestant ones. He had brought French troops with him after all, and the Irish came to his aid. So he waited for William to come over and give battle.

But William thought, shrewdly, that he and his wife had better consolidate their position by being crowned first. It was a joint ceremony and to mark it, Colonel Churchill was created Earl of Marlborough, thus giving him the first step upward toward his final title of Duke. The faithful Bentinck was given the English title of Portland, which his descendants still use today.

But to Mary, the whole Coronation was a nightmare. She had been standing there in her robes, with her maids twisting the last strand of pearls through her hair, ready to leave her room and join William, when a page tapped at the door.

The lady in waiting in attendance went to see what was the matter and came back with a letter in her hand. "This arrived a few moments ago, by express, your Majesty."

Mary tore the letter open. The sight of her father's own writing made her feel faint and tremble. The words swam before her eyes, so that she could scarcely read them. Yet she knew she dared not let anyone else read such a letter out loud to her.

She forced herself to read: "Hitherto I have been willing to overlook what has been done, and I thought your obedience to your husband and compliance to the nation might have prevailed. But your being crowned is in your own power; if you do it while I and the Prince of Wales are living, the curses of an angry father will fall on you, as well as those of a God who commands obedience to parents."

She felt the curious eyes of her dressers upon her and crumpled the letter up hastily. Then with head held high she left the room to take her place with William at the head of the procession. She must not fail William. But afterward, she found that not one word of the ceremony, not the cheers of the crowds, had made any impression. Only her father's curse.

During that spring and summer, King James strove hard to regain his crown. On July 1 of the following summer of 1690 William, who had crossed over to Ireland with a large army, defeated him at the Battle of Boyne, and James returned to France, never to make another attempt. It was only when autumn came again, that Mary's anxieties over her husband's safety quieted down. When he came back to her, they began to discuss where they would live.

Whitehall and St. James's were too near the city fogs for William's chest. So they bought Kensington House, a pleasant little building, then a few miles out of London.

Wren, the great architect, was told to turn it into a palace, and he did. But it was Mary who, with her husband, planned the gardens which give Kensington Palace its oddly Dutch appearance today.

If the Prince of Orange—now crowned William III of Great Britain—ever felt homesick for his own country, he hid the fact as well as he could. Mary, born and brought up in England, found herself casting many a backward glance over her shoulder. She made cleanliness and order in the English palaces and brought in the new fashions for cheerful chintzes and delicate china. And by that autumn, things had quieted down enough for William to turn his thoughts to his favorite hunting.

The sport here in England was tame to that of the great forests of Guelderland. There was little excitement in staghunting compared with hunting wild boar. And the green Forest of Richmond, where King Charles and his friends had found sport enough, was too tame and civilized. Still, it would have to serve. . . .

The trees were no longer green now. In the orchard of Richmond Palace, the leaves drifted gently down and the ripe fruit began to glow on the branches. Sarah, Countess of Marlborough, looked up at them and laughed.

"Do you remember when I treed you up there, for refusing me an apple?"

"I remember, Madam," Mr. Gibson said grimly. He wore his fine plumage again; this time a suit of hunters' green with a silver belt and a silver buckle in his hat. His quick eye had been scanning the apples on a bough almost touching his head. He jerked one off, polished it on his sleeve, then presented the rosy side of it to her. "Let me make amends now."

She took it and bit into it. The next moment she had spat the bite out and thrown the apple on the ground. "You little devil! 'Tis wormy!"

He dodged her uplifted hand and ran after Mary and Anne who had gone on ahead. Mary turned to smile at him and beckon him to walk along the path between them. There was no room for Sarah when she reached them and she had to take to the grass. Mr. Gibson, swaggering along between the Queen and the Princess, gave her a malicious grin.

Now they had passed through the gateway in the orchard and stood looking down on the forest. No longer were they young enough to lift up their skirts and run down the tilted fields toward the shadow of the trees. A carriage stood waiting to take them there.

Sarah, already sulky at being crowded off the path, announced that she wanted no more exercise; she was going back. Mary raised her eyebrows at this, for Sarah was supposed to be in attendance on Anne. But Anne as usual let Sarah take her own way, and my Lady Marlborough soon vanished, while the dwarf, who knew he had contributed to her ill-humor, climbed delightedly onto the box beside the coachman.

The carriage stopped on the fringe of the trees. The two sisters got out and proceeded slowly down the pathway that opened before them. They heard, far away, the long notes of a hunting horn. Except for that it was so quiet the golden leaves falling made a rustle as they alighted.

Anne said, "I think the new stuffs you have hung in your apartments look exceedingly strange. Cotton instead of silk! Your taste has grown foreign, Mary."

Mary said, "It is what William likes."

Anne glanced sideways at her tall sister to see if she had taken offense, but apparently not. So she ventured, "Not that I dislike all foreign things. Tea, for instance."

Mary smiled, slipping her arm through her sister's. "You shall have another box——"

She broke off. "What is that man doing there?"

It might only have been the shadow of a tree. But the path had widened, to let a shaft of light strike through. And at the end of it, where it twisted out of sight, stood something like a man.

Anne shaded her eyes and said, "It's a tree."

But the shadow moved forward, coming to meet them. And Mary caught her breath suddenly. Somewhere, long ago Monmouth had stepped out from the trees. For one breathless second she thought time had not only stood still but gone backward. . . .

To still her agitation and bring back sanity she said sharply, "You see, it is moving toward us, so it's a man."

"I still think it's a tree," answered Anne, her mouth set in the obstinate line that her sister knew so well.

But Mary did not hear. The man had stepped free of the deceptive shadow which had made him look so much taller than he was. She recognized William, and was already running down the path joyfully to meet him.

Epilogue

Mary Stuart, great granddaughter of that other, more famous Queen of Scots, began the joint rule with her husband at the age of twenty-seven. During William's necessary absences abroad to visit his own country, she ruled with dignity and firmness. Nor did she forget her interest in bringing education to the new colonies beyond the seas. She must have spoken of this often to her husband for him to receive a certain clergyman from Virginia so kindly.

Here is part of a letter from the Reverend James Blair, describing his reception at the Court of William and Mary:

London. December 3d, 1691.

It was Novr. 12th, in the Council Chamber, before the Council sat. I was introduced by the Archbishop of Canterbury and my Lord Effingham. . . . I kneeled down and said these words. "Please your Majesty, here is an humble supplication from the Government of Virginia for your Majesty's charter to erect a free school and college for the education of their youth." So I delivered it into their hand. He answered "Sir, I am glad that Colony is upon so good a design and I will promote it to the best of my power."

So was founded the College of William and Mary in Williamsburg, Virginia.

Mary never saw her father again. He kept a shadow court near Paris, bitterly resentful of the behavior of his two daughters. Mary's half brother, the baby Prince of Wales whose birth had brought about the change of rule in Great Britain, grew up to claim its throne in his turn. But his Rebellion of 1715 was put down, as was that of his son the glamorous Bonnie Prince Charlie, thirty years later.

By that time both William and Mary were long dead. Anne, who had succeeded them, was dead too. Mary died of smallpox in December 1694. When William heard there was no hope for her, he fainted. His grief was so intense, they thought at first that he would not survive her. But his iron self-discipline forced him to recover and continue the duty of governing the country for seven years more, until his own death in 1702.

Yet still the words which burst from him in his first agony at the thought of her death, come down to us as Mary's best epitaph. "From being the happiest, I am going to be the miserablest creature on earth. I have never known a single fault in her."

BOOKS FOR FURTHER READING

Sarah Jennings Churchill
Kenyon, F. W., GLORY AND THE DREAM. New York, Dodd,
    Mead and Co., 1963.
Kronenberger, Louis, MARLBOROUGH'S DUCHESS. New York,
    Alfred A. Knopf, Inc., 1958.

Grizel Hume
Kyle, Elisabeth, STORY OF GRIZEL. New York, Thomas Nel-
    son and Sons, 1961.

James, Duke of Monmouth
Blackmore, R. D., LORNA DOONE. New York, Dodd, Mead
    and Co. (Great Illustrated Classics)

Samuel Pepys
Pepys, Samuel, PEPYS' DIARY. J. P. Kenyon, ed. New York,
    The Macmillan Co., 1963. (This title is also available in
    a paperback edition—New York, The Macmillan Co.,
    1963)
Varble, Rachel, THREE AGAINST LONDON. New York, Double-
    day and Company, Inc.

William of Orange
Ogg, David, WILLIAM III. New York, The Macmillan Co.,
    1956.
Robb, Nesca A., WILLIAM OF ORANGE, A PERSONAL PORTRAIT,
    Vol. I. New York, St. Martin's Press, Inc., 1963.